# EPH HANKS
## FEARLESS MORMON SCOUT

# IVAN J. BARRETT

Covenant
Communications, Inc.

This book is based on the life of Ephraim K. Hanks and has been carefully researched. However, the story is fictionalized and does not purport to be accurate in every detail.

Library of Congress Catalog Card Number 89-081998
Ivan J. Barrett
*Eph Hanks, Fearless Mormon Scout*
First Printing February, 1990
Third Printing August 1994
ISBN 1-55503-210-9

Dedicated to my editor, Darla Hanks Isackson, and to all the descendants of Ephraim K. Hanks. May this book help them to know Eph better and to live better, inspired by such noble ancestry.

# 1

# THE RUNAWAY

On a hot summer day in Lake County, Ohio, the blue eyes of Ephraim K. Hanks looked down the endless rows of corn he had yet to hoe. Eph (as he was usually called) was twelve years of age and the twelfth son of Benjamin and Martha Hanks. Taking off his straw hat and wiping the sweat from his forehead, he felt Ring, the farm dog who had picked Eph as his own, nuzzle against his leg and whine. "No, Ring," Eph said with feigned earnestness. "No, Ring, 'taint no use to beg. Pa told us boys to hoe ten rows each before we leave the field. My brothers are way ahead of me. Quit pestering me. I don't like this any more than you do." But Ring prolonged his high pitched whine, whimpering his protest so convincingly that Eph decided, "Well, why don't we go hunt our squirrels now? We can hoe the corn after that."

Eph dropped his hoe and picked up his gun propped against the trunk of a maple tree near the corn patch and ran with Ring at his heels into the woods. By mid-afternoon with six squirrels in his hunting bag and a sheepish grin covering his mouth, Eph slowly walked back to the corn field. The sun was too hot for his brothers to continue hoeing the weeds from between the corn rows, so they scurried to the shade. Sometime afterward, father Hanks arrived to inspect the work. After counting the rows, he observed the poorly weeded ones far outnumbered the well-hoed rows. Pointing to the rows which had been carelessly cultivated and looking sternly at his sons, father Hanks asked, "Who hoed these rows?"

Hoping to escape a hide tanning, one of the boys blurted out, "Eph did."

The other boys echoed, "Eph did! Eph did!"

The father looked at Eph with a twinkle in his eye, "You must be tired, Eph, after doing all these rows and shooting all those squirrels. Take the squirrels up to the house and clean them for supper." Turning abruptly to the other sons, he said sharply, "You boys better hoe over these rows again and do a better job this time!"

When Eph was six his father often sent him on errands. He was dependable and quick to respond. Eph's brothers were jealous of his good fortune in being their father's helper, especially when Eph was selected to assist his father in the roadside blacksmith shop. Before long, he was blowing the bellows. By the time he was twelve he had learned to fit shoes on horses and make trap springs and do almost everything a blacksmith was expected to do. Throughout Lake County he was known as "The Young Blacksmith." Eph's brothers taunted him and complained that their jobs in the fields were more difficult than his work in the blacksmith shop.

By the time Eph reached the age of sixteen his father entrusted him with important assignments. One Saturday he was asked to drive over to River Ridge to collect a sizeable amount of money a man owed his father for work done for him in the blacksmith shop. Eph hitched his father's favorite mare to a new carriage and sitting in the driver's seat, big as you please, he trotted the mare down the road. Not far from his father's farm he picked up a friend to accompany him on this entrusted errand.

The man at River Ridge handed Eph the amount of money he owed his father, and the two boys began their return trip home. A feeling of importance came over Eph, and he decided to show off the fast-trotting mare and let people see the new buggy he had helped his father make. His friend suggested they ride over to visit a mutual friend some miles out of their way, and Eph liked the suggestion. "Why not? The afternoon is just getting under way." But before they left their friend's place, dusk shadowed the trees, and the stars commenced to twinkle above the darkening sky. The mare was forced to run fast and upon reaching Eph's father's barn, was white with lather, agitated by the fast pace she had been forced to take, and was frothing at the mouth.

The next morning Eph's pa walked in the shed to

feed the animals. When he saw Ol' Bess covered with dry lather and mud he was mad as a "yeller hornet." He rushed to the boy's bedroom and collared Eph, asleep by the side of an older brother. "Out of there, you young rascal."

Half asleep and startled, Eph asked, "What's wrong, Pa?"

"What's wrong? You mistreater of my favorite mare. You damn near killed her. I'm goin' to punish you good for that!"

"Oh, Pa, I'm sorry. I'll never do it again. Don't punish me."

"The Bible teaches that if you spare the rod you spoil the child, and I ain't going to spoil you, Eph. It's a good thing for you today's the Sabbath, but tomorrow I'll wallop ya good. Let's get ready for the revival meetin' in town."

"I don't feel like goin', Pa."

"Well, stay home then," returned father Hanks.

As one of the older brothers was leaving the house to join the family in the big wagon, he sneeringly asked, "Ain't ye goin' to the revival, Eph?"

"No, I feel sick."

"You'll be a lot sicker after Pa gets through with ya. Put Bailey's Dictionary under your pants and ya won't feel Pa's leather strap," he guffawed as he scurried out the door.

Eph propped his feet against the mantel above the fireplace. He was miserable and perplexed. "Pa and I have been the best of friends, partners in the blacksmith shop, but I ain't going to stay and get walloped by the Pa I love," he mused. Watching the dying embers in the fireplace he made the decision to run away. Tying a few clothes in a bundle and picking from the pan three biscuits his mother had baked for the Sabbath meal, he left the house, called Ring, glanced his farewell at the old homestead, and walked briskly up the road.

His heart may have tugged to stay home, but the seat of his breeches urged him to move fast northward along the dusty road toward Lake Erie. His pace didn't slacken although the calves of his legs tightened and his left leg cramped until he gritted his teeth with the annoying pain. The sun descended into the west, and Lake Erie glowed like a bright reddish ball of fire. Darkness gathered over the area and his stomach growled with hunger. He had long since devoured the three biscuits. The yellowish moon all but jumped out of the ground and for hours lighted the roadway as Eph trudged northward. Were the moon made of green cheese, as he was told when a little boy, he wished he had a hunk of it to munch on. As Eph reckoned, it was three in the morning before he dropped on the ground in a wooded spot near a creek for a few hours' sleep, using the bundle of clothes for a pillow, and Ring curled by his side.

The sun was high in the sky when Eph awakened. Ring had run out, possibly after some quail or some of the many birds chirping in the trees. Fortunately for Eph, he hadn't moved after he had awakened. Turning his head to the right, he saw coiled within inches of him a large rattlesnake flipping his tongue at him but not sounding a warning rattle. Eph was glad Ring had run off and hoped he'd stay away until the rattler crawled away from him. Near his hand was the heavy stick he'd used as a walking cane. He was tempted to grab it and whack the rattlesnake over the head, but sensing the quickness of the snake, he figured it would strike before he could get the stick, so he lay perfectly still, his heart pounding against his ribs. He would try and out-stare the venomous reptile, but the snake kept his head near Eph, his black tongue flipping. Then, to his horror and amazement, the rattler slithered up on his chest as Eph lay breathless and motionless. He was scared, but not enough to make even a slight movement. Out of the corner of his eye he watched the snake crawl slowly and felt it nestle on his rib cage and look into his eyes. Eph's heart was pounding so hard he hoped it would knock "the damn thing" off. After a few seconds—which seemed an eternity to Eph—the rattler moved over his cheek and slowly crawled away toward the creek. Just then Ring came bounding to Eph with a fat quail in his mouth. Eph was so paralyzed after the snake episode that it was a few minutes before he could pat Ring on the head and commend him for bringing in the quail.

Eph cleaned the quail, built a fire, roasted the bird, and enjoyed a light breakfast with Ring. The sixteen-year-old lad walked on through the trees laden with dew teardrops that bespoke of color and beauty. That morning the Lord had made the world all too beautiful. It was "charged with the grandeur of God." Nature had never been more inviting to Eph, despite his seeming regrets at times about leaving home.

Shortly before noon Eph walked into the village of

Perry and stopped at a blacksmith shop along the roadside. In and around the shop loitered five loafers, telling yarns and spitting tobacco juice. The loafers eyed him with an obtuse glance but said not a word. His stomach growled with hunger; and hoping to earn money to buy some food, Eph walked up to the blacksmith who was shaping a long piece of metal at the anvil and asked if he might blow the bellows for him. The workman eyed him questioningly, spat a squirt of tobacco juice into the ruddy coals, and beckoned him with a nod of his head and a wave of his hand to go to work.

The blacksmith was making trap springs to be used on carriages. This type of work was what Eph had specialized in at his father's shop. In the process of making the springs all went well until the smithy began to bend the spring to test its firmness. No sooner had the spring been bent than it snapped like a broken twig. After breaking the third spring, the blacksmith imagined Eph was a jinx to him.

Eph spoke up and offered, "Mister, let me try making one." The smith, dubious of the outcome, hesitated in replying.

One of the loafers, with an anxious expression, called out, "Let the boy try one. He can't do any worse than you've been doing."

"Go ahead, boy," exclaimed the disgusted blacksmith. Eph put the slab of steel into the hot fire as he had done many times before. Afterwards the smithy shaped the steel until it was ready for tempering. Eph took from his pocket a small package of white fever powder. His mother always insisted her sons carry fever powder with them just in case they had a rise of body temperature above the normal. With two fingers and a thumb he drew out a pinch of the white powder and sprinkled it into the water of the tempering trough. With the smith's tong, Eph placed the steel into the hot forge and heated the metal to a glowing red. Then he quickly withdrew the heated steel from the forge and dipped it, sizzling and sputtering into the water trough. As he withdrew the steel, the eyes of the smithy and the loafers were fastened on him. Placing his foot on one end of the metal he bent the spring down and held it taut in the curved shape for a moment. When he released his foot the spring bounded to the ceiling. The loafers chuckled with pleasure, and one spoke with sudden emotion, "The boy is an expert." Even the smithy was pleased and commended Eph.

"Boy, where did you come from?" the blacksmith inquired.

"Oh, down the road a ways."

"Why are you here away from home?"

"I'm sixteen now and decided to make it on my own," said Eph firmly.

"Does your Pa know you're goin' on your own?"

Eph hesitated before he answered. Then he blurted, "Naw, he and I had a misunderstanding and I pulled out unbeknownst to him."

"So, you're a runaway! What's your name?"

"Eph Hanks," Eph slowly replied.

"Come to the house with me, Eph, and my wife will fix you a good meal. You must be famished".

Young Hanks readily responded. A few bones were

thrown to Ring by the woman of the house. Eph relished every mouthful served him. While he was gorging himself, the blacksmith asked if he would stay and work with him in the shop.

"I want the work in the most way, but I'm too close to home for comfort. Pa might learn where I am and come get me," said Eph.

The blacksmith readily understood. "I think I can help you get a job with Mr. Chambers who lives in Unionville some miles northeast of here. He's comin' to my shop this afternoon, and he might give you a job."

Eph helped the blacksmith until late afternoon when Mr. Chambers arrived. After hearing Eph's story and the blacksmith's recommendations, Chambers decided to employ Eph on his farm—then he asked Eph, "Your dog don't bite, does he?"

"No, sir, Ring is a friendly animal."

Eph thanked the blacksmith for his kindness, climbed onto the wagon seat next to Chambers, and rode away to Unionville.

The Chambers household also included Mrs. Chambers and a blind girl named Helen, who became Eph's best friend. Nothing was too good for Eph. He worked hard chopping wood, milking cows, husking corn, and hauling hay. One day when the work on the farm was done, Chambers invited Eph to go squirrel hunting with him.

Observing his keen marksmanship in hitting a squirrel with every shot, Chambers allowed Eph to hunt whenever he was not encumbered with jobs on the farm. Squirrel meat became the staple diet for the family, and Eph relished the way Mrs. Chambers prepared it in her outdoors oven.

Eph's clothes became almost threadbare, and Mrs. Chambers turned her husband's old shirts and pants inside out and made them over for the squirrel hunter.

On the 4th of July, Eph borrowed a horse to ride to town for the celebration. Amongst the observers of the national holiday Eph met Bill Reed, whom the Hankses had reared from childhood. Bill was five years older than Eph. They were delighted to see each other. Bill was working on the Erie Canal and had his pockets full of money. Seeing the makeshift clothes Eph was wearing, he escorted him to a store and purchased his friend a new outfit.

Bill insisted Eph join him and work on the Erie Canal. The farm boy was anxious to do so but felt he should return and bid the Chambers family goodbye. The farewell was with much sadness. Helen had become dearly attached to Ring, who had proven a seeing-eye dog for her, and Ring responded to Helen even more readily than he did to his master. Mr. Chambers asked Eph to leave the dog with his daughter, and Eph consented.

With a lump in his throat, Eph bade farewell to his friends and walked up the road, looking back occasionally to see Helen holding onto Ring and Mrs. Chambers waving goodbye.

Reaching Buffalo, New York, with Bill Reed, Eph was hired to drive the horse which pulled the boat carrying freight between Buffalo and Albany along the bank of the Erie Canal. Looking at the forty-two-foot wide canal with water four feet deep flowing on its twenty-eight-foot wide bottom, Eph gasped and said, "Bill, this is quite a ditch!"

"Yeah, it is quite a ditch. That's what the people who opposed the digging of it called the canal—'Clinton's ditch'—because Governor DeWitt Clinton was the man behind its construction," explained Bill.

"How long is this big waterway?" asked Eph.

"Three hundred and sixty-three miles. It connects the Atlantic Ocean with the Great Lakes."

From Buffalo, Eph drove a big bay horse which drew eastward the sixty-foot boat filled with raw materials. Going downstream, Eph kept the rope slackened to let the horses drawing the boats upstream walk over it. The men working on the canal were a rough, tobacco-chewing, foul-talking bunch. They showed no respect and considerable contempt for Eph because he was a sixteen-year-old boy.

Determined to maintain his rights and status, Eph tangled with a horse and driver of a boat going downstream. During this entanglement, the horse of the other boatman was sent sprawling into the canal.

"What the hell—!" yelled Joe, the driver of the dislodged horse. Bill and Eph leaped into the canal and tugged at the floundering, solid-hoofed mammal to get it back on the bank. Joe and the two other men of the downstream barge assisted. When the doused horse clambered up the bank, Joe, with clenched fists, walked over to Eph and snarled, "I'll knock the hell out of you for this, boy!"

"You lay off this boy," snapped Bill and took a

swing with his doubled fist at the aggressor. Fists began
to swing. Heavy blows were exchanged. Both fighters
were on the edge of the canal bank and were about to
plunge into the water. Eph caught Bill by his left leg
and dragged him away from his opponent who pitched headlong into the four feet of canal water. After being pulled out by his two mates, gasping for breath and
completely soaked to the hide, he shook his fists at Bill
and Eph and threatened, "This clash is only the beginning of troubles for you buggers."

"We'll string you two worthless cusses up to the
rafters of the warehouse the next time we see you
there," Joe's two pals added threateningly.

A few weeks later while Bill and Eph were
unloading their boat at the Rochester Canal delivery
station, the three ruffians entered the storage shed.
Rushing toward Bill and Eph, they succeeded in grasp-
ing Bill. Two of them held the struggling Bill while Joe
threw a rope tied with a slipknot around his neck. Eph
grabbed a two-tine pitchfork on the floor near him and
rushed over to where the three ruffians were holding
Bill. He pinned Joe with a tine of the fork on either side
of his neck and pushed him to the wall. With a well-
aimed kick on Joe's shins, he released him with a swift
jab of the pitchfork at his posterior. At this moment Joe's
two companions rushed toward Eph. Eph thrust his
pointed weapon at them, and they fled with Eph at
their heels, stabbing them in their buttocks. Days went
by before these scamps sat down when they ate their
meals.

Bill and Eph handled loads of freight and operated

their canal boat until Lake Erie froze over. The last time the five men met, Joe extended his hand to Eph and shook it with gusto. "You sure made good on this job, young feller."

"Thanks," Eph returned.

In Boston, Eph and Bill met a recruiting officer for the United States Navy. "Boys, there is a great future for you in the navy. Have you ever imagined seeing the exotic lands of the world—Europe, Asia, the Orient? You will when you join the navy. And you'll not only see the sights of the world, but you'll get a fine education and good wages. Come and join us."

Eager for adventure, the young men set sail on the *U.S.S. Columbus* the last of October, 1842. A few days after leaving the Boston harbor, Bill and Eph began to understand clearly that they were in the navy for a three-year stretch. Obedience must be rendered to the officers. Bill showed Eph stripes on his bare back from a cat-o'-nine-tails for not obeying an officer's command. Eph liked the sea and loved sailing. At times he helped the ship's blacksmith. His principal job, however, was learning to be a sailor.

Sailors were expected to patch their clothing and do their own sewing. To Eph this was sissy stuff, but there was no other course for him to take. Once, when he was sitting on the deck mending his carry-all sack, three sailors not much older than he sauntered near him and leaned against the top rail around the deck. One boy grabbed the thread and jerked it out of Eph's hand. The spool rolled across the deck. The mischievous fellow laughingly pointed to the rolling spool and shouted, "Look at it go!"

Eph reached for the thread, and a second tantalizer stepped on his hand while the third rowdy snatched the white cap from Eph's head and sailed it across the deck. The three antagonists then spat into the cap. Eph boiled with anger and muttered between his lips, "These damn rogues ain't goin' to get away with this!" Casting his eyes around the deck, he spied a belaying pin. Leaping off his haunches, he seized the pin and rushed over to the three trouble makers. He whacked one of them on the side of the head and knocked him sprawling on the deck. A second fellow sprang toward him, and Eph laid him low with a sharp swing of the belaying pin. Before he could take a cut at the third chap, the fellow clutched Eph about his middle, and the two struggled fiercely for supremacy. As they grappled, they fell down the hatchway. Regaining their equilibrium at the bottom of the hatch, they exchanged heavy blows. A stern orderly briskly walked up, grabbed each young man by the shoulder, and pulled them apart. "Break it up, you unruly tars!" he bellowed.

The next day when an investigation was made to determine the cause of the rumpus, the officer in charge, after hearing the details, said to Eph, "You're a tip-top lad. You certainly gave those bullies what they deserved."

On the upper deck Eph liked watching the big blue man-eating sharks as they followed the *U.S.S. Columbus*. The tale got around that the sharks followed a ship persistently when they sensed approaching death. Eph was aroused to fever pitch with the urge to catch one of those large, voracious fish. Finally he could hold it within no longer and was impelled to ask the captain if he might try his luck at catching a big blue shark. The captain, with a chuckle, replied, "Go ahead if you think you're lucky."

In the ship's blacksmith shop Eph shaped a strip of iron into a hook. Tying the hook on a strong rope, he pierced a hunk of pork for bait, fixed a block and tackle, and threw his contraption overboard.

The bait had barely struck the water when a greedy shark swallowed the pork, hook, and part of the rope. Eph began his pull and yelled for the other sailors to give him a hand. The entire crew became so excited that some were on the verge of jumping overboard.

"Pull together, boys," ordered the first mate, "and you'll have the big fellow on deck."

With grunts, violent pulls, heaves, and quick gasps for breath, the sailors hoisted the big, sharp-toothed fish out of the water and dumped it flapping and lashing onto the deck. Before the blue shark was dispatched, it seemed as if it would dash the ship to bits.

The captain said with an oath, "No more fishing for sharks, Eph!"

During a heavy storm at sea, Eph and two other sailors were dashed from the topgallant yard into the rigging below. One sailor struck his head against a heavy object and was instantly killed; the other lad was swept overboard. Fortunately for Eph, he grabbed a dangling rope on the side of the ship, swung himself to the trembling railing, and was rescued by his mates. This marvelous escape put Eph as a hero in the eyes of the crew, and he enjoyed the best the ship could offer.

Eph's three years of enlistment in the navy came to a close, and he was in a quandary whether to return home or re-enlist. The *U.S.S. Columbus* docked at the New York pier. While Eph and other sailors were working at the pumps, a strange man dressed in gray tweed clothes walked up to the sailors and, ignoring all but Eph, spoke to him and used his influence in persuading the young sailor to return home. Eph then had his trunk transferred to a ship headed for Boston.

Eph and his fellow sailors decided to go ashore and into the big city of New York. Eph, who had taken to the stranger in gray tweed, invited him to join them. He declined. After Eph and his fellow sailors finished their fun and purchased a few trinkets, they returned to the ship just before the gangplank was lifted. From the pier they saw the man in the gray tweed sitting on Eph's trunk; but when Eph reached the trunk, the man was gone. No one had seen him leave the ship. The stranger was gone but not the influence he had left with Eph.

# 2

---

# THE CONVERT

After meeting the mysterious man in the gray tweed suit, Eph felt a strong compulsion to return to his father's home in Ohio as quickly as possible. This anxiety increased to the moment he reached the gate in front of his childhood home. He hesitated; "How can I approach Pa and Ma and my brothers whom I have not seen for over three years?" he mused. The warm glow of the light from the window beckoned him in. Pushing the front door open, he tiptoed through the living room into the kitchen. His mother was putting supper on the table. Her glance caught sight of her tall, husky two-hundred pound sailor boy standing in the doorway. She gasped—was she gazing upon a ghost? She quickly regained her composure; and Eph held his mother in his arms and, with tears trickling down his cheeks, kissed her warmly.

During the supper with his mother and brothers, Eph was saddened by the news that his father had died less than two years after Eph had gone to sea. This was a terrific shock to Eph, whose esteem for his father had greatly increased during his years as a sailor. Experiences had developed in Eph the steadying element of character, and his father had been elevated to a high status in his mind. He had longed for the day when he could be reconciled with his father.

More disturbing news awaited Eph. Sidney, his older brother, had been led away by the terrible Mormons. They were holding Eph's favorite brother in a trance, enslaved without a hope of escape or freedom. The thought of his brother being a helpless victim of the degenerate Mormons, duped by the fraudulent prophet, Joe Smith, angered the sturdy sailor; and he resolved he would find Sidney and free him from "those awful Mormons."

To Eph's surprise, Ring, the dog he had given the blind girl, Helen Chambers, had returned home over a year before. Desiring to visit the Chambers, Eph, with his brother, Lige, and Ring, drove in a carriage pulled by a team of bay horses to the Chambers' farm in Unionville. The dog recognized Helen and licked her face. As the blind girl cried for joy, she kissed Ring. Eph assured the Chambers he intended to leave Ring with Helen. Mr. Chambers told Eph that he and his wife were growing old and offered Eph his farm and all belongings connected with it, if he would stay and take care of Helen. This was a tempting offer, but the influence left on him by the man in the gray tweeds was driving him forward to new adventures. After declining Mr. Chambers' offer, he bade Helen and her parents farewell and the two brothers returned home.

Immediately after returning home, Eph set out for the Mormon city along the Mississippi River in Illinois to rescue Sidney. Traveling a day and a half, he came to two forks in the road. He started down the right fork. A strange power bewildered him. Tears streamed from his eyes, blocking his forward movement. Something was wrong, so he turned and took the other fork. The same queer, unexpected feeling overpowered him. Stepping off the road into a grove of sycamore trees, Eph knelt in prayer. For the first time in years he implored his Heavenly Father for help. His mind cleared; he was no longer confused. He retraced his steps home.

Opening the door, he saw his brother Sidney. Delighted, the two brothers embraced each other. Surprised and amazed, Eph discovered that his brother was not a dupe but was bubbling with the spirit of the restored gospel of Jesus Christ. Sidney unfolded to his widowed mother and his brothers the principles of life and salvation as revealed by the modern prophet of God—Joseph Smith. When nigh unto death he had been healed through the administration of the servants of God.

This doctrine aroused the resentment of their mother. She requested Eph to bring to the house the two most able sectarian preachers who could be found in Lake County to controvert Sidney's dogma.

The ministers arrived. An argumentive discussion ensued, but Sidney ably maintained his position. His mother and brothers sat on the side of the sectarian preachers. Accurately quoting from the Bible, Sidney soon had his opponents so confused and discomfited that they resorted to abuse and slander. "Young man," one shouted, "Joe Smith is a liar, a thief, and a false prophet. Anyone who would follow him would steal from his own mother!"

Eph had been a silent listener; but now, excitedly aroused, he grabbed a chair and, pointing to the door, ordered the preachers to leave. These men of the cloth departed so quickly that one of them left his silk hat. Eph followed them to the gate. They stepped hurriedly into their carriage, applied the whip to the horses' backs, and streaked away up the dusty road.

Upon returning to the front room, Eph saw his mother crying. He asked her to forgive him for forcing the hurried exit of the two abusive ministers. "But, Mother, no one can slander my brother while I am here. We live in a free land where a man has the constitutional right to believe what he pleases without abuse."

Early in the morning Eph was splitting logs and chipping them into fireplace lengths when Sidney walked up to him, smiling with downright amusement. "Ho, there. I wonder if those preachers are still running?"

"If they're not, they should be, if I have my way," replied Eph. The two brothers laughed heartily. Sidney related a dream he had had in Nauvoo, Illinois, which had made such an impression on his mind that he returned home to learn the meaning. When he beheld his long-absent, seafaring brother, the interpretation became clear.

Sidney's unfolding of the Mormon religion struck a responsive chord in Eph's breast. There on the woodpile that day he decided to cast his lot with the Mormons. This decision became the turning point in Eph Hanks's life.

Mother Hanks felt so upset over the spiritual trouncing by Sidney and the physical ousting by Eph of the two preachers, that she told her two sons plainly that they were no longer welcome in the old Hanks homestead. So Eph and Sidney bade their mother farewell and outfitted themselves for a long journey to the Mormon city of Nauvoo. Eph was in his twentieth year—a strong specimen of young manhood. He was spiritually minded and possessed in his youth the gift of prophecy. He was destined to perform a work on the frontier of civilization which would cause the savages to look upon him with wonder and amazement. He was amply qualified for the work Providence had marked out for him.

Eph was thrilled with the new message given him by Sidney. It glorified God and put man as His child in a position to enjoy Him forever. For the first time Eph understood God as a glorified man and Jesus as literally the Son of God who lived in mortality in the image of God. Eph had found a new grip by which he could hold on to the power of God. This spiritual force pulled at his entire being. He resolved to be a defender of the gospel, of Zion, and the cause of God—come what may.

The two brothers traveled together until they

arrived at Indianapolis. Here they separated—Sidney making his way to Nauvoo and Eph journeying to Chicago to be with his friend Bill Reed who had been discharged from the navy one year after the two boys had enlisted. Bill had settled in Chicago and was firmly established in the hotel business. Their meeting again was one to be remembered. Nothing was too good for Eph. Bill insisted Eph join him in the hotel business, but Eph's thoughts centered on the strange people called Mormons. While working with Bill, Eph heard the disturbing news of the martyrdom of Joseph Smith and his brother Hyrum. This news upset him greatly, and the urge to mingle with the saddened Mormons and be a comfort to his brother Sidney became stronger each day.

One day Eph said to Bill, "I must go to Nauvoo. I am an unbaptized Mormon, and I must be with my people."

"Stay with me, Eph. I will pay you high wages. I will do everything I can to keep you with me in Chicago."

"Thanks, Bill. You are a dear friend, but my soul cries for the truth to be found only in Nauvoo." With a warm embrace the two friends parted.

Eph was amazed at the beauty of the city built under trying circumstances by the much belittled people. Every Mormon in Nauvoo was busy—the completion of the temple was strenuously pushed. He lost little time in applying for baptism and was baptized by Horace S. Eldredge in the Mississippi River. Shortly after his confirmation he was ordained a seventy in the Melchizedek Priesthood.

Eph met Brigham Young, the chief apostle, who, with the other members of the Twelve, assumed Church leadership. There grew from their first meeting a feeling of kinship which would endure throughout their lives. When Brigham Young advised the Saints to prepare for a long journey westward, no one heeded this advice more eagerly than Eph Hanks.

At Mount Pisgah in Iowa Territory, Eph joined the Brigham Young pioneer company. Here he learned from his file leader that the United States had declared war on Mexico and President Polk had sent Captain James Allen and Colonel Thomas L. Kane to raise a Mormon army of five hundred able men to march to California and assist in the conquest of Mexico. Eph was among the first to volunteer his services.

Eph reasoned he was better able to make the march to California—since he was not married—than many of the other men who had wives and children. His years in the navy had prepared him for hardship, and he had the strength to endure.

Brigham Young counseled with Eph and Sidney before the Mormon Battalion march commenced. He congratulated Eph on his quick response to the call of duty and promised him the Lord would protect him. Sidney was counseled to remain with the body of pioneers and assist in the westward trek. He advised Eph to send his army money to his brother to further the movement west.

The send-off for the battalion volunteers was elaborate. Everyone had a cheerful countenance. A farewell ball was given with most everyone participating. In the mid-July sun they danced Virginia reels, sang songs, made merry, and prayed. The advice of Brigham Young to the young soldiers was accepted fully by Eph Hanks. Brother Brigham told them to be true to their country and to God. He prophetically declared, "You will not be required to shed human blood. Remember your prayers, refrain from profanity, obscene language, and improper use of the name of Deity. Burn your playing cards. Be strictly virtuous. Never take that which does not belong to you—even from your enemy."

At Fort Leavenworth the Mormon soldiers obtained muskets, ammunition, and provisions. The fact that every man could write his own name was a surprise to the officers in charge. On August 12, 1846, the battalion left the fort on its long march to the Pacific coast. Their march was saddened with much sickness and a few deaths. Being blessed by the Lord with the gift of healing, Eph was often called upon to administer to the sick. The army doctor forced the Mormon men to take calomel for every complaint. One day the "quack" left pills for Eph's companion to take. Eph loaded the pills into his musket with some powder and shot. At close range he knocked over a sage hen. The two young men enjoyed sage hen for supper. The next day, Eph's companion was well and took his place in the ranks.

Eph and his fellow soldiers endured the long marches even though they were tiresome. Often they were without water for days. Many of the weary soldiers were unable to keep the pace during the day and had to walk part of the night to catch the company before break of camp the next morning. Often when water could not be found, it was necessary for the able men to dig wells to save all the soldiers from perishing.

In the latter part of January, 1847, the Mormon Battalion reached Warner's Ranch near San Diego and viewed the Pacific ocean amidst shouts and exclamations of "We have arrived!" Eph and his comrades were overjoyed with the warm sunshine and abundant vegetation which, coupled with cool water from mountain streams, added immeasurably to their comfort.

# 3

# THE TOREADOR

"What is that so deep-blue and glimmering below us?" excitedly asked Hollister Rogers.

"Why, that's the Pacific Ocean," shouted Eph Hanks. "Boys, we've reached our destination."

"Hurrah, hurrah! God be praised!" chorused over two-hundred male voices.

The Mormon Battalion, after trudging two thousand miles through a wilderness where only savages and wild beasts roamed, over deserts where water was scarce, over mountains covered with snow and temperatures near zero, without a guide over this trackless terrain, at last reached their destination of California. They had dug deep wells so the travelers after them could also refresh themselves. With crowbars and picks, Eph and his fellow soldiers had cut their way through narrow chasms of living rock and over elevations which seemed to defy aught except the wild goat. They brought the first wagons from Santa Fe to the Pacific and had laboriously herded the invaluable mules without loss. The Mexican garrison of four presidios within the walls of Tucson gave them no hesitation. The battalion drove them out without firing a shot, and Eph vividly remembered Brigham Young promising them they would not be required to shed human blood. These Mormon men and boys had marched half-naked and half-fed, often living on wild animals while in the service of their country in a declared war against Mexico.

Looking upon the blue Pacific, Eph recalled Brigham Young, the chief apostle, taking him aside at the Mormon campground at Council Bluffs and congratulating him upon his quick response to the call of his country and promising him that the Lord would be with him. At the same time Sidney was counseled by Brother Brigham to remain with the main company of Mormons and assist them on their westward journey.

All the money Eph could spare from his pay as a soldier had been sent to Brother Sidney to further the travel to the Rocky Mountains. Eph and his fellow soldiers had followed the counsel given them by the President of the Twelve Apostles. They had their prayers night and morning; they had refrained from profanity and obscene language; they had been strictly virtuous and respectful of property and person in their march through enemy territory. Now, the last of January, 1847, the Mormon Battalion marched into

San Diego and was overjoyed with the warm sunshine, the verdant vegetation and the cool mountain streams.

The Mormon soldiers were ordered to repair broken-down buildings, make roads and walks, and build a church for the villagers. These tasks were sheer drudgery to Eph; he longed for more exciting experiences.

One day a Spanish fiesta in honor of St. John's Day brought much excitement to San Diego. A parade began the festivities with richly dressed Spaniards from neighboring haciendas leading the procession, showing off their fancy high-prancing horses. Gaudily attired Mexicans brought up the rear. Following the parade, cock fights and horse racing swept the attention of the people. Even with this excitement everyone was chattering about the bull fights in the afternoon.

Eph and his fellow battalion boys soon caught the spirit of the gay holiday and became as excited as the participants. In their patched and worn-out clothes, they looked shabby and insignificant compared to the ornately dressed Spaniards. A few of the younger Mormon soldiers were listening with rapt attention to a fervent discussion about the toreadors who were to fight the bulls that afternoon. One of the principle voices in the discussion turned to the Mormon boys and jeeringly remarked, "Perhaps one of these Americanos would like to fight the bull."

Bill Caspar spoke up. "From the experience we had with the wild bulls in the cane-grass country, we should be qualified to fight your bulls."

The Spanish man laughed sarcastically. They chaff-ed the battalion boys about being afraid of bulls. Eph Hanks stepped up to them and said, "Get us some good horses, and we'll show you what Americanos can do."

Senor Hernandez, a mild gentleman who had been a silent listener, volunteered to furnish Eph and Bill two horses for the afternoon amusement. He invited the two young Mormons to be his guests for the day. At his mansion they were introduced to his charming daughter, Conchita. She was much concerned over these two young, inexperienced Americans engaging in the dangerous sport of fighting a mad bull. She endeavored to persuade her father not to let the young men risk their lives in such a fatuous venture. But Eph and Bill were determined to enter the bull area as matadors.

News spread that two American soldiers were go-ing to be picadors and prod the bull in the arena that afternoon. Some of the Mexicans doubted the two young Americanos would show up for the bull fight. However, the arena was jammed, and the spectators were intensely excited when Eph and Bill rode into the ring. What the spectators viewed that afternoon was unusual, notable, dramatic, and entertaining. The bull rushed out of the pen with head erect; snorting, paw-ing the ground, and bellowing its challenge to the two greenhorns who rode their horses expertly to stay out of the reach of the enraged bull's horns. To the surprise of the onlookers, the two young men outguessed the black bull in its every charge at them.

Suddenly the angered bull wheeled on Bill unexpectedly, forcing the horse against the high rampart below the stand occupied by the spectators. To the horrified audience it appeared that the bull would surely gore the horse and rider. The ladies covered their eyes and gasps were heard all over the crowd. Alert to the danger Bill was in, Eph spurred his steed to rescue his friend from the enraged bull. Seizing the huge bovine critter by the tail, with a mighty jerk he turned the bull around, giving Bill a chance to ride to safety. The throng shouted and cheered and threw armfuls of flowers into the arena as a token of praise for this unexpected feat.

At the gate of the enclosed area for entertainment, waiting for the two bull fighters to exit, were Senor Hernandez and Conchita. They insisted that Eph and Bill accompany them to their hacienda. The young Mormons long remembered the feast they ate with the Hernandez family. Conchita stood at Eph's side during the elaborate meal, serving him smilingly. This made Eph rather uneasy. After the banquet, Senor Hernandez motioned for Eph to follow him into his private room. With his arm around Eph's shoulder, he showed him a bag of gold and a bag of silver. "My brave Americano, half of this gold and silver is yours if you will marry my Conchita. If you will become my son-in-law, I will give you half of all the calves and colts branded on my ranchero."

Eph swallowed hard and gasped in surprise. "I thank you for this generous offer, Senor," he said. "Never have I seen a more beautiful girl than your

Conchita; but, sir, I must return to my people whom I left months ago on the Missouri River, for I have a sacred commitment to them." When Senor Hernandez perceived Eph's resolute firmness to leave California for the Mormon community, he graciously presented him with ten saddle horses and a complete pack and riding outfit. He expressed his hope that someday his young Mormon friend would return to San Diego.

Some of the battalion at San Diego, including Eph and Bill, were ordered to the presidio Los Angeles, a military post, to exterminate the wild dogs which were overrunning the village. Some time after the battalion boys had rid Los Angeles of the canine pests, they made friends with a number of Mexican villagers. Not knowing that Eph and Bill had established themselves as champion bull fighters, there were those Mexicans who considered the Mormon soldiers inexperienced with horses.

In this part of the village, the Mexicans had a wild, spiteful burro controllable only with two lassoes. This donkey charged with open mouth and red eyes any man he saw. One day the Mexicans cleverly brought the beast securely lassoed onto the street in front of a cafe. They offered Eph five dollars to ride the burro and not be bucked off his back. Eph took their offer.

The Mexican men blindfolded the burro and held the beast fast until Eph got astride, and then the mischievous troublemakers scampered to safety. The lassoes were released, and a young man jerked the blind from the burro's eyes and dashed through the doors of the cafe with the burro snorting on his heels.

Eph, holding tightly to the mane of the unrestrained quadruped, rode through the swinging doors. A large mirror much valued by the owner of the cafe leaned against the counter. The burro, seeing himself in the glass, stopped for a moment and then, with teeth bared, plunged head on, smashing the costly mirror into bits of broken glass.

The customers fled in mingled confusion out the back door, followed by the owner carrying a bowl of soup he did not have presence of mind to release from his hand. The burro thrust his head forward with open mouth for the seat of the cafe proprietor's breeches. Just then the proprietor was grabbed by two Mexicans who had climbed onto a low roof and pulled out of the donkey's reach. Two battalion boys enjoying Eph's prowss as a burro rider grabbed a lariat off a tethered horse's saddle, expertly roped the animal, and shortly had it subdued. The Mexicans who had bargained with Eph had fled to the roof of a low adobe house. They were totally amazed when Eph found them and collected the five dollars. The cafe owner didn't return to his eating place for two days.

The battalion boys were given their honorable discharge from the United States Army at Los Angeles on July 16, 1847. With ten fine horses and the pack and saddle outfits given him by the rich Spaniard, Eph led the way to Sutter's Fort on the American River some three hundred miles north of Los Angeles. En route they met a man named Smith who had accompanied Samuel Brannon east from San Francisco to meet the Mormon pioneers and attempt to persuade Brigham

Young to come to California. Smith told them there were five hundred wagons on their way to the Salt Lake Valley, but Brannon failed to induce Brigham Young to bring the Mormons to the Pacific Coast. This was the first news the Mormon Battalion soldiers had heard of the westward trek of the Saints.

Arriving at Sutter's Fort, Eph and his fellow battalion soldiers found opportunities for employment at good wages. A number took advantage of the job offers and remained to work for Captain Sutter. Eph and others started their journey eastward. Leaving the basin of Lake Tahoe, they met Samuel Brannon returning to California from his meeting with Brigham Young. He gave the battalion boys a doleful account of the semi-desert region Brigham Young was leading the Mormon pioneers to and predicted the final removal of the Mormons to California. He urged all of the Mormon Battalion to return and work at Fort Sutter until spring.

The next day the volunteers met Captain James Brown, ranking officer of the Pueblo detachment of the battalion. Eph eagerly inquired about the welfare of the men and families who spent the winter in Pueblo, and Captain Brown informed him they had joined President Young and the pioneers, and when he left they were near the Great Salt Lake Valley. Brown had letters for many of the battalion. Eph received a letter from Sidney. From it he learned Sidney wouldn't be with the apostles and the pioneers as he had specific assignments at Winter Quarters. An epistle from the apostles advised the battalion men who had no means of subsistence to remain in California and labor during the winter, bringing their earnings with them the next spring to Salt Lake Valley. About half of the men accepted this suggestion and returned to Sutter's Fort. But Eph and others spurred their horses on to the Salt Lake Valley.

# 4

# EPH'S ROMANCE IN THE VALLEY

On the sixteenth of October, 1847, Eph and his companions pulled the reins of their horses' bridles taut and dismounted in front of Pioneer Fort in the Salt Lake Valley. The fort had been built by the pioneers of logs and sun-dried bricks called adobe. All openings of the fort were on the inside of the enclosure, and each house built within the fort had a small lookout for the occupants to see Indians, were they to approach. The roofs of the houses were made of poles covered with brush and dirt.

Walking to the high log gates of the east entrance, the battalion boys were met by "Father" John Smith, chosen on the 3rd of October as president of the Salt Lake Stake of Zion. He was accompanied by a half dozen battalion members who had arrived in the valley with the pioneers the latter part of July. Such a warm greeting of hugs and tears has seldom been seen before or since. They were welcome to occupy some one-roomed houses not lived in within the fort. Eph and a few other unmarried men preferred to camp outside the fort.

The next day was the Sabbath. Eph attended the services held within the fort. One of the bishops made a speech, warning the teenage girls to beware of the battalion boys who had just arrived from California.

"Those young lads will try to marry you and then carry you off to California away from the Saints of God."

Eph was infuriated; all night he chafed over the unjust advice of the narrow, bigoted bishop. At daybreak he saddled his horse and rode through the open gate of the fort to the front door of the bishop's house. He pulled his horse around and backed him into the door, hitting it with resounding force, breaking the latch, and forcing it open. The bishop jumped out of bed, his wife screamed with fright, and the children screeched in terror. The indignant Eph sternly warned, "I give you one week to retract what you said about us battalion boys. If you don't, you won't have one log left standing on your house. Remember, one week or down it comes."

"Oh, my, sir!" exclaimed the frightened bishop. "I will retract! I will retract!" Some time after this he told his friend, "I could see house logs in Eph's eyes!"

Fortunately, the first winter in the Great Salt Lake Valley was a mild one. By dint of untiring energy during the fall and winter, Eph, with the other adult brethren, constructed nearly twelve miles of fence, which made an enclosure of more than five thousand acres and included the main part of the city plot. About 200 acres of fall wheat was sown. The winter being mild, plows were rolling the earth throughout every month of winter. Eph plowed and planted a few acres of his own land near the mouth of Cottonwood Canyon. He and his fellow colonists noted with joy that the grain sprouted early in the spring, and the prospects of a bounteous harvest were good. The latter part of April, President John Smith requested Eph to carry an important message to Brigham Young, en route from Winter Quarters on his second journey to the mountains with over two thousand Saints. Eph had scarcely departed from the valley when large black crickets swarmed down from the foothills by the millions and began devouring the freshly growing fields of grain.

Every way possible was utilized to destroy the ravenous pests. Holes were dug, the women and children drove the black crickets into them, and they were buried with dirt. The men plowed ditches around the wheat fields, turned the water into the ditches, and drove the hopping insects into the running streams to be carried from the fields. They destroyed them by the thousands, but all to no purpose. Fires were built and hordes of the pests driven into them, but with little success. Each day more and more swarmed down the hillside. Failure to destroy the crickets meant famine to the settlers in Salt Lake Valley. John Young said despairingly to President John Smith, "Send a fast rider to overtake Eph Hanks and inform President Brigham Young of this plague, advising him not to bring more Saints to the mountains to die of starvation."

"No, Brother John," responded John Smith. "We'll not send a messenger. God did not bring us here to die. Call the Saints together, and we'll pray to our God for deliverance."

Then the miraculous happened. From the Great Salt Lake came flocks of seagulls, their shrill half scream, half plaintive cry heard by all who were on their knees. The seagulls hovered over the wheat fields. They flew down and began devouring the crickets. The upper feathers of the gulls' wings were tinted with gray and black. Their white breasts and heads were gratefully observed by the Saints. They swooped down and gorged themselves with the loathsome insects. After glutting themselves with crickets, the gulls flew to the nearby streams, drank, vomited, and returned to the fields. They ate gluttonously again and again until the plague was stayed and the crops of the pioneers saved.

On Sunday, the fields were deserted by the Saints who devoted themselves to worship the God who had sent them deliverance from the cricket disaster. Monday morning they visited their fields and saw on the edges of the ditches pile after pile of dead crickets.

When Eph returned after delivering the message to his friend and prophet Brigham Young, he learned of the cricket plague and the miracle of the seagulls and was much surprised to find his wheat crop ready for harvest. He whispered reverently, "God be praised."

President Young and his company of 1,229 souls

arrived in Salt Lake Valley on September 24, 1848, and he preached to the Saints in the forenoon of the Sabbath. Brother Brigham, knowing of Eph Hanks's qualities as a frontiersman, tested his obedience on many occasions.

One morning as Eph was at work building an adobe house in the fenced-off portion of the city, the Prophet drove up in his carriage. Without stepping out of the carriage, he called, "Eph, how thick is that rock wall around your house?" "Eight inches thick, Brother Brigham." His leader said, "Tear it down, Eph and build it twice as thick." Without another word or glance Eph's way, he turned his carriage around and drove off. Eph had hauled rocks from Ensign Peak for a number of days. He had paid, from his battalion pay, a mason to lay the wall with lime mortar. He dreaded the work of tearing down the present wall and putting up a thicker one. Also, the expense of building another wall was almost more than he could afford.

The mason was markedly upset and swore with the remark, "Brigham Young may be a prophet, but he's no builder of stone walls!" But Eph rehired the mason to double the width of the wall and started hauling more rock. Thirty days later the sixteen-inch wall was up. As the rafters were being put in place a heavy storm arose. Rain poured down until streams flowed in every direction. Soon the basement of Eph's new house was flooded. But the sturdy sixteen-inch walls stood firm. A few days later as Eph nailed his rafters on, he thanked the Lord for His prophet and the good sense he had to obey him.

In late October at an evening dance, Brother Brigham called Eph over to where he was standing on the sideline of the many dancers and said, "Eph, go home and shave." Eph had not cut his beard in several months. It was brown and wavy and almost reached his waist. He liked to stroke the soft hair and felt pride in having a beard so long and thick. Without a moment's protest Eph walked to his room, took a last look in the mirror, caressed his favored whiskers, and then with the scissors and razor cut off his prized possession. However, he left a heavy mustache.

He ran back to the dance hall. When he entered, almost everyone greeted him with boisterous laughter. But not the Prophet who frowned and chided, "Did I not ask you to shave?"

Eph nodded, "Yes sir."

"Well, go back and do it right," ordered Brother Brigham.

Without a word Eph did as he was told.

The Prophet Brigham found in Eph Hanks a young man who gave strict obedience no matter what he was requested to do. Here was a man whom he could trust to do any mission given him and who could serve his prophet in every way needful for the building of the latter-day kingdom of God.

The gold rush to California of 1849 brought many gold-seekers overland to Salt Lake Valley. A wagonload of men stopped in front of the old tithing office in the growing town of Salt Lake. A big bully yelled from the wagon that he would lick the first damn Mormon he saw. Eph Hanks happened to be that Mormon. Eph, who was then a young man, looked up at the bully and said, "Come down, boy. Come down off your wagon."

The big bully shouted to his wagon mates, "I'll go at him."

Eph replied, "Here's your chance." That same big bully an hour later had one of the soundest whippings a braggart ever had. Unassisted and without a missed punch Eph used his navy training, much to the amusement and entertainment of the bully's friends and a few of the Saints standing by.

Eph had a cousin living in Illinois whom he never met. This cousin was quite a fighter, especially as a wrestler. His name was Abraham Lincoln. Eph never looked too far on the Hanks family tree or maybe he'd have become acquainted with that cousin.

Eph's training from his blacksmith father and his portable blacksmith shop kept him in touch with the passing immigrants and their unshod mules and horses. Blacksmithing was a real resource throughout Eph's life among the Saints. Also, it made him bad medicine for weaklings and bullies.

Pioneers—and Eph was one of them—are restless and energetic. Unsatisfied, they forge ahead, always finding something different to do, and Eph led them all.

Eph took pride in his California horses. He delighted to show them off to the Saints in Salt Lake City. When he rode down the streets, people often gasped, "Oh, what a beautiful palomino horse you are riding, Eph! She looks like a newly minted gold-piece." When he rode his chestnut Arabian with a white star in his forehead and white strips on the front legs, the admiration of the bystanders was even more pronounced.

One June evening astride his Arabian saddle horse, Eph rode by four girls strolling along the roadside. One of them, a raven-haired, dimpled young lady called out, "What a beautiful horse! Won't you give us a ride?"

Eph pulled the horse up short, saying, "Whoa, Star—this young woman wants a ride!" He dismounted and helped the girl who had spoken into the saddle, then he swung himself behind her, and the two rode briskly off to a new friendship which turned to love.

"I guess you think I'm a brazen hussy to ask you for a ride," said the girl, "but I couldn't resist the chance of riding your beautiful Arabian horse. I have a great love for horses."

"Why, Miss, I think nothing of the sort. You are a lovely girl, and I'd like to know your name," replied Eph.

"I'm Harriet Little. Since I was a little girl I enjoyed helping my father care for his horses in England."

"You're an English girl?"

"Yes, we were converted to the Church by Elder Lorenzo Snow and immigrated to Nauvoo shortly after the martyrdom of the Prophet Joseph and his brother, Hyrum."

"I'm disappointed I didn't get to meet you in Nauvoo before we started west to California with the Mormon Battalion."

"Oh, you're a soldier, are you?"

"No, I'm a rider of fine horses which I had given me by a Spanish gentleman in California. I'm a lucky fellow, for this Arabian horse attracted you to me."

Eph learned that Harriet was a young widow living with her parents, the Deckers. Later that evening as he stopped in front of her home and assisted her off his horse, he asked, "May I spend tomorrow evening with you, Harriet?"

"Yes, Eph, I would be pleased to have you come see me. Please come in time for supper."

"What time's that?" eagerly inquired Eph.

The next day dragged slowly for them both. Eph was in love for the first time in his life, and he could hardly wait until he saw that lovely English girl again. Following the counsel of the Prophet Brigham, he shaved his face and put some sweet smelling perfume given him by Conchita behind each ear. Dressed in his California suit and riding boots with a cravat around his neck, he mounted his palomino, after saddling the Arabian for Harriet, and rode to the Decker house fifteen minutes before supper time. Harriet introduced Eph to her parents. The meeting was mutually impressive. Eph put on his best manners at the table. At the close of the supper, Eph offered to help with the dishes.

"Goodness, no," said Mrs. Decker. "Harriet has on her riding clothes. You young folks go for a horseback ride. I'll do the dishes."

Father Decker spoke up, "My boy, I'll help with the dishes. Next time you can do them alone."

"Oh, no," chipped in Harriet. "I'll help if Eph is involved."

With a pleasant goodbye the two young lovers rode down the wide street and galloped east toward Mill Creek. Here Eph showed Harriet his wheat field, golden with ripened grain, and a four-room adobe house almost finished. The setting was ideal. Within a short distance was the canyon with a refreshing breeze ruffling the ebony hair of lovely Harriet.

Eph glanced at the English girl and mused, "Was there ever such a beautiful girl? She is for me only." Then he spoke. "Would you like to go into the house and suggest how we might furnish it?"

"We?" exclaimed Harriet with a gasp. Eph smiled, and they both laughed heartily. "Why not?" asked Harriet, and Eph assisted her from the chestnut Arabian.

Into each room they went. Harriet suggested a comfortable chair by the fireside, a built-in cupboard on the opposite wall, a nice table with four chairs in the center of the room.

"I guess," said Harriet with marked enthusiasm, "this room is the kitchen, isn't it?"

"Why, sure," admitted Eph.

She offered many suggestions for the living room off the side of the kitchen and the two bedrooms on the west side of the house. While standing in the doorway, facing the east mountains, Harriet said, looking up into Eph's gray-blue eyes, "Never think it was your horse that attracted me to you."

"It wasn't the Arabian?"

"No, I should say not. When I saw the handsome, clean-faced rider I said to myself, 'He's for me.' Then there was your manly chest. I never saw a chest on the other young men, for theirs were covered with grisly beards. But yours I saw strong and manly. May I look again at your clean-shaven face? Other young men's faces are all whiskers."

"Do so, Harriet," invited Eph. "And speaking of my manly chest, I'm going to hold you to that."

He drew her into his arms and kissed her lips warmly. Then he quickly said, "We'd better get you home. Your parents will think I'm keeping their daughter out all night."

"Oh," sighed Harriet, "let us linger a little longer in the twilight together."

With an arm around her waist, he escorted her to the horses and gently lifted her into the saddle on Star's back. Together in pleasant silence they rode back to the Decker home. From that evening through the summer the two lovers were seen together frequently. The long summer evenings with the katydid's shrill sounds and the bright moon shining were ideal for courting.

One morning in August, Eph came to the Decker home unannounced. He rapped softly on the front door. There was no response from within, so he walked around the side of the house to the garden. There at the well curb was Harriet, drawing a bucket of water with a rope on a pulley. She was whistling. A clear sound of a hymn came from each forced passage of her breath. Eph stood by the corner of the house listening so intently he scarcely drew a breath. Then with the pail of water in her hand, Harriet turned to walk to the house and saw Eph.

She almost dropped the pail. Her face turned crimson red as she gasped in much embarrassment, "Did you hear me, Eph?"

Eph, wanting to make the most of it, looked very

sternly at her and said, "Whistling woman, crowing hen."

The red commenced to burn more noticeably in her cheeks. It was the brightest red Eph had ever seen. As he directed his glance at her, he could see she was much ashamed. But to Eph she had never looked so sweet and pert.

An idea struck Eph's head, and he said, "A whistling woman in Mormon land brings sure harm. Only one thing will break the spell."

"What is that?" humbly inquired Harriet.

"I hate to tell you, Harriet."

"Why?"

"Because it involves me."

"How?" asked Harriet.

"Well, I'll come out with it. To break the charm, Harriet, you must be kissed by the man who heard you whistle. This alone will set you free from the portent evil."

Harriet was blushing, but she answered sweetly, "Please come, Eph, and break the charm and set me free from the annoying penalty."

Eph took her in his arms and kissed her many times. Harriet pushed him away and said with mock harshness, "Oh, you stop, you stupid boy. You just caught me whistling once."

At that time they decided to get married. Father and Mother Decker readily approved. Preparations were made, and on September 22nd they were joined in holy matrimony by the man whom Eph admired most, the Prophet Brigham Young.

# 5

## DODGING INDIAN ARROWS

Utah Valley for many years had been the annual gathering place for all the Ute Indian bands from valleys over a region of two hundred miles. Fish swam up the streams from the large freshwater lake in enormous numbers to spawn every spring. Suckers and mullet galore passed as if to fill the rushing water from bank to bank. The Indians feasted on the abundance of fish from morning until night. Besides feasting, the redskins raced horses, traded, and gambled for weeks.

In the spring of 1850, when the Indians gathered and found white men had settled in their favorite "sports" valley, Chief Walker of the Utes was furious. He talked to Big Elk of the powerful Timpanogas tribe. "White man is no good. He robs us of our land, our fish, our horse racing, our good time. You, Big Elk, get rid of white man, so next spring we will not see them here."

Big Elk also was a hater of the whites and fond of fighting. He said to Chief Walker, "I will kill all whites. I will steal grain, cattle, and horses. Don't worry, Walker, we will fix 'em."

Shortly after the Indian bands departed from the valley by the fresh water lake, Big Elk and his braves ran off cattle and horses from the herds of the new white settlers of Utah Valley. Settlers going outside the fort built on the west bank of the Provo River were shot at. Many were the times arrows fell uncomfortably near the fuel gatherers.

Stock continued to be taken, and all efforts to recover them were vigorously resisted by the Indians. The Timpanogas band was well supplied with firearms and ammunition which they had acquired in exchange for horses from California emigrants passing through to the gold fields.

President Brigham Young received reports of these Indian depredations and asked his trusted friend, Eph, to ride down into the valley and talk with Chief Big Elk and persuade him and his braves to stop stealing and live in peace with their white Mormon neighbors.

Two rides to the Timpanogas camp in Utah Valley were made by Eph without results. Eph determined his third trip would be his last. President Young had always counseled, "Shed no blood," and Eph hoped to avert bloodshed with his final appeal for peace. Eph rode his prize palomino into Big Elk's camp near the mouth of a canyon. As he stopped near Big Elk's tepee, two husky braves rushed over and seized his palomino by the bit on each side of his head. Staring fiercely at Eph, with war paint streaked across their faces, they snarled, "You no in-e-to-ah!" (Get away!) Eph's trained eye took in the entire encampment of the Indians. Sitting on a high ridge, with his gun pointed straight at Eph was a dusky Indian. Such a precarious situation would destroy the courage of many men, but Eph had experienced several tight spots and he knew how to outwit the Indians.

Without any marked concern he sternly said, "Me at-am-bar ne-ab." (Talk to the chief.)

Chief Big Elk emerged out of his tepee with an arrow stretched on the bowstring. Talking in the Indian's language, Eph said with firmness, "Big White Chief say, 'You stop bothering peaceful white man or he send army and wipe you out! No more Big Elk!' "

Surly Big Elk grunted, "Isk-in-nish t-shaker. Coin ne-ab pan-now-rup puckage quent-sen-poach!" ( I say, me fix Big White Chief like this.) He shot a number of arrows through a large buffalo robe. Pointing to the warrior on the ridge he added, "Towadq-ka aukage puck-ki-teah-kuoaha!" (Big brave with loaded rifle kill you and horse.) And he laughed satanically.

Eph tried again, "Pieka tig-a-boo tsong quap!" he pleaded. (Come, let's be friends...smoke pipe of peace.)

"Katz!" (No!) growled Big Elk.

Knowing his words were ineffectual in moving the old chief to live peacefully with his Mormon neighbors and sensing the Indians had planned to kill him, Eph quickly thought of an escape plan. Sharply he lashed with his quirt, striking the heads of both the braves who were holding his horse's bit. He spurred his palomino and raced for a wooded ravine. The Indian on the ridge aimed at the fleeing Eph and fired. Fortunately, his aim was not accurate, yet the bullet struck the stirrup, missing Eph's foot by a fraction. Big Elk pulled taut on his bow string, and an arrow flew after the galloping palomino. It pierced Eph's coat as it sped between his sleeve and body.

Racing down the ravine, Eph thanked God for his safe escape. Suddenly he heard the pounding of horse's hooves just behind him. Glancing back, he saw a white charger overtaking him, and on its back was the man in gray tweeds. "Could it be?" thought Eph, "Or is it a cloud of dust?" The hoof beats died away. Eph rode alone across the flat, well out of rifle range of the Timpanogas Indians. He was unable to reach his home in the Salt Lake Valley before the next day. Harriet, who was alone with their two little children, had spent much of the night praying for his safety. She told Eph upon his return, "I received great comfort from a quiet voice of a man who spoke to me and said, 'Do not fear for your husband's safety, for I was with him today.' "

As Eph held her in his arms, she continued, "I fell asleep instantly with no more fear."

"I know, dear," replied Eph, as he caressed her in his arms. "It was the man in the gray tweeds."

Chief Big Elk and his warriors continued to steal cattle and horses from the Mormons in Utah Valley and to badger the settlers. Eph was given but ten minutes' notice that he was to help quell these Indian uprisings. Bidding his Harriet a hasty goodbye and assuring her not to worry, for the man in gray tweeds would be near him, he saddled his horse and joined Captain George Grant with fifty other brethren and rode south to the Provo River.

The Timpanogas Indians, led by Chief Big Elk, were camped in thick brush, well protected. Before sunrise Eph and his companions surrounded the Indian camp. George Bean, Indian interpreter, was dispatched to order the Indians to surrender so that no blood would be shed. Before Bean was heard by Big Elk, a number of his hot-headed braves, viciously excited, fired at the white men. This ended negotiations. The battle had begun.

Fierce fighting raged between the red men and the whites. On the second day of battle, Eph and fourteen other fearless men were ordered to charge the Indian enclosure. In the attack in the thick brush, Eph's horse was shot from under him. Two arrows pierced his Navajo blanket coat. Although the white men were in close range of the Indians, the red fighters resisted the charge with few casualties. Night came on. Big Elk and his warriors made a hasty retreat toward Utah Lake. Eph and the other white men were alerted and rode furiously in pursuit. The fleeing Indians were overtaken. The majority were taken captive. During this frightful battle, Big Elk and fifty of his braves were killed, but only one white man was lost.

When peace was restored between the Timpanogas Indians and the Mormons, an old Indian came to Eph's home one day, and, recognizing Eph, he said, "Me big brave with Chief Big Elk. Me aim two shots at your heart—no hit. Great Spirit grab bullets, you no fall to ground."

Eph soon learned that to understand an Indian, one had to think as an Indian. The Mormon settlers had come on to the land the Indians considered their own. They felt the Great Spirit had given it to them. White man should not occupy Indian property. One Indian said to Eph, "Mormon cattle eat grass seeds. No grind seeds. No eat bread. Eat Mormon cattle instead. White man kill Indian. Indian kill white man. Indian poor. Mormon rich. You give; all right. No give; we take."

Eph learned a fact spurned by many men, that understanding the Indian was the only possible way to peace. To learn to understand and consequently love these dark-skinned natives of the mountains was the only sure way to conquer hate.

This great fact was taught to Eph when the Prophet Brigham called him to accompany Jacob Hamblin and other robust Mormon men to the Tooele Valley, west of Salt Lake, and put down Indian depredations against the village of Tooele.

Time and again the Indians had broken their promise not to steal Mormon cattle, and their thieving had been a heavy loss to the Tooele settlement. So Eph and Jacob Hamblin decided the savages had a lesson coming. With the first fall of snow, the opportunity arrived. The presiding elder ordered Eph, Jacob, and the other men, ". . . to kill every Indian found, and bring none into the settlement."

The men decided to travel by night and secret themselves by day and to watch every pass and mountain defile. On an upper bench, the wily chief and his braves were surprised the second morning. They scattered to the foothills like quail. "Split up and keep them from the mountains," was the order. Eph and the others wheeled their horses in wild and reckless pursuit. In a box canyon, Eph spied an Indian take to his heels up a rough ledge. To get him on horseback was impossible. There were treacherous rocks and underbrush between the pursuer and the pursued. Eph tethered his horse deep in a pocket hidden from Indian view, grabbed his rifle, and began the chase. Eph had no idea how many braves there were in that canyon. Eph selected the safety of a huge rock at the opening of a narrow pass. He had not long to wait.

Cautiously the Indian approached. Eph, hidden from the Indian's view by the huge rock near a steep ledge, awaited him. Within fifty feet of Eph, the Indian turned and saw Eph as he raised his rifle to his shoulder. Before the Indian could fit an arrow to his bow, Eph took careful aim and pulled the trigger, but the gun misfired. In frantic haste Eph snatched a fresh cap from his pouch, re-cocked the hammer and trigger, but fumbled at the mashed and useless brass of the un-fired cap. The Indian, aroused to his precarious plight, sent an arrow whistling under Eph's arm, nicking his coat sleeve. Eph snapped the trigger again without result, and another arrow pierced the crown of his hat. The gun jammed. A third arrow whizzed past his head. Eph grabbed a rock and let it sail at the dark-skinned enemy. It knocked him sprawling. The Indian ran, stumbled, fell, and tumbled over and over down the slope to the bottom of the ravine. Eph waited alertly for an hour, but no more Indians showed themselves.

When the men gathered back to the place from which they had scattered to pursue the Indians, Eph learned that not one man was able to discharge his gun within range of an Indian. One of the Mormon men received a slight arrow wound, which was the only injury inflicted. The Holy Spirit forcibly impressed upon Eph and the others, especially Jacob Hamblin, that they were not to shed the blood of the aborigines but were to be messengers of peace to them.

For eighteen years Eph experienced days that tested his soul, but he emerged triumphant from the ordeal. As he crossed the plains east with an important message sent by the First Presidency of the Church to the president of the British Mission, Cheyenne Indians robbed him of everything he had—his horses, his supplies, his guns—all except the clothing on his back and a butcher knife concealed in his bootleg pocket. Hundreds of miles from Salt Lake Valley with few travelers on the Oregon trail, he wondered what to do. This would perplex the most resourceful mind. But Eph continued on his way on foot as if nothing disastrous had happened. Inside his coat pocket was the message to the British Mission president. Failure to carry that document to the missionaries who would deliver it to its destination might cause much sorrow and trouble. Eph knew he was on the Lord's errand. He had been promised by his prophet friend, Brigham Young, that his mission would be successful.

He walked on, his trusted dog by his side. With his feet sore and his body wet with sweat, he came to a mountain stream hidden from view by heavy underbrush. Refreshing himself from the cold clear stream, he spotted on the south bank a short distance away a herd of buffalo warming themselves and chewing their cuds in the noonday sun.

Stealthily Eph crept along the south bank of the stream until he came close behind the resting herd. With cat-like agility he sprang behind a full grown buffalo cow lying down and cut one hamstring. He ran to a narrow ravine along the bank with the buffalo mad on his heels. The buffalo stood pawing madly, the ravine being too narrow for her to enter. Eph's dog ran out and nipped at the back legs of the bison. The cow turned to charge the dog, and Eph slipped out of the ravine and cut the other hamstring. After killing the animal, he jerked as much of the meat as he could carry and continued walking.

Down the road he sighted a camp of Indians belonging to the Cheyenne tribe which had robbed him two days before. He located the herding ground without their being aware of his presence. During the late hours of the night, Eph caught two of the finest steeds among the Indian horses and by daylight was thirty miles on his way. Arriving at Fort Laramie the next day, he obtained from the army officers a good traveling wagon. He arrived in St. Louis several days before the departure of the missionaries he was meeting.

During the summer of 1858, Eph, with his Indian man Yodes, was returning from California after delivering important mail for President Brigham Young. Eph camped near a beautiful clear lake high in the Sierra Nevada Mountains. Yodes took care of the mules while Eph commenced to make camp. The sun was sinking in the west, and its bright reflection mirrored the lake. Eph glanced into the looking glass-like lake and noticed something moving above his campgrounds. Observing more closely, he made out the shadow of an Indian watching from a ledge.

Without turning or indicating in any way that he had seen the spying Indian, he observed several more redskins. Yodes had the mules unharnessed and the camp utensils almost unloaded. Eph nodded to Yodes and whispered, "Harness the mules as quickly as you can." His Indian man complained, "You just told me to unharness them." But he hurriedly threw the harnesses on the mules' backs as Eph loaded the camp utensils quickly into the wagon, all the time watching the evasive movements of the shadowy forms.

Traveling down the bumpy road as fast as the weary mules could go, Yodes was shaking his head, mystified. They were suddenly surrounded by a dozen young Indian braves who were armed with bows, arrows, and tomahawks. Their faces were streaked with war paint, and with war whoops and shouts, "Puck-ki T-shuker boin!" (Kill whiteface!) they were brandishing their weapons. Eph knew they intended to kill him and Yodes. Speaking their language, he tried to make peace with them but to no avail. A "Me want to ts-gib-a wub." (Scalp.) drowned Eph's peace proposals.

Since the moment Eph observed the movements of the shadows of hostile Indians on the surface of the lake, he had prayed inwardly. Now, a flash of inspiration came to him. Being acquainted with the ways of the Indians, Eph knew that they were afraid of crazy people. A tradition existed with them that if such a one were killed by an Indian, the Great Spirit would destroy the whole tribe.

Eph jumped up in the wagon, waved his arms frantically, and talked wildly to the Great Spirit, "Yenno ads me e-iqueay!" (Have them hand to me their bows or they die). Then, cupping his hand over his right ear, he posed as if he were listening to the answer from the Great Spirit. He swung his hand around and threw it up in the air, "Katz-oats to Great Spirit!" (Take my hat.) Removing his coat, he threw it off, shouting, "Here tah!" (Here's my coat.) Then to the Indians he shouted, "Great Spirit heap tobuck!" (Great Spirit heap angry.) Eph pulled at his hair and beard snarling, "Me tur-reb-by tots-sib-awub!" (Me throw away hair!) He tore off his shirt and flung it into the air, but when he started to take off his trousers, the Indians turned with frightened whoops and hastily retreated.

Eph and Yodes resumed their homeward journey without further trouble. Riding along, Eph chuckled to himself, being rather proud of how well he had played the part of an insane man. Yodes said, "Eph, you heap crazy white man! Heap crazy!" and he laughed in the guttural Indian way.

# 6

## "THAT HANDCART COMPANY IS IN TROUBLE. WILL YOU HELP THEM OUT?"

In October, 1856, Eph contracted to deliver a load of fish for the Salt Lake market. Fish were abundant in the Utah Lake some forty miles south of his home. After a few days of fishing in the fresh-water lake, Eph commenced his drive to Salt Lake with his wagon box brimming over with various kinds of fish. By late afternoon he arrived at Draper and spent the night with his friend, Gurney Brown. Eph was weary after the strenuous journey and retired early to the bed allotted him. Although fatigued, he could not sleep. His mind was troubled with thoughts of the late-coming handcart company long overdue in Salt Lake Valley. He knew from experience traveling the plains and mountains in winter, how much the snowbound handcart Saints must be suffering. He tossed and rolled about in the bed, unable to sleep. Ghastly visions of men, women, and children suffering on the bleak Oregon trail obsessed him. Shortly after the clock struck one in the morning, Eph dozed into a troubled sleep.

Abruptly he was aroused by a voice calling his name. "Eph! Eph! Eph!"

"Yes," he drowsily answered and opened his eyes, expecting to see Gurney Brown. The room was dark and empty of any human beings. He lay back on the bed and dozed once more. Again the voice called his name. Again he answered. There was no one there. Could he have dreamed he heard a voice call his name? He lay pondering. His mind troubled but his body weary, he dozed once more.

The third time his name was called in sharp penetrating tones. Startled, Eph set up. "Yes, yes. Is there something I can do for you?" He heard the voice clear and definite say, "That handcart company is in trouble. Will you go and help them?"

Eph sprang out of bed, hoping to see the messenger. He thought, "Was it the man in the gray tweeds? If it was, he has gone." The request was certain, and Eph would comply. He dressed quickly. Gurney Brown and his wife, Lucy, awakened and inquired what was wrong. Eph quickly related the urgent request for his help for the stricken handcart people. The Browns assisted him and, putting a sack of flour and warm clothing into his wagon, bade him goodbye.

Eph drove into Salt Lake City as the dawn was breaking over the Wasatch Mountains. A messenger dispatched by President Brigham Young met him with the urgent request from the Prophet that he go immediately to the rescue of the distraught handcart company. The Prophet was pleasantly surprised to know Eph was in the city. He was warmly greeted by the Prophet who laid his hands on the able mountain scout's head and blessed him with strength and endurance to reach the afflicted handcart pioneers and bring them relief.

Delivering the wagon load of fish to the market and driving home to bid his beloved Harriet and children goodbye, the intrepid Eph drove out and up the canyon with a light wagon filled with supplies. Eph was alone.

The violent snowstorm, blowing fiercely from the east which had brought so much suffering and loss of life to the handcart people, enveloped Eph near the South Pass. The heavy snow impaired his progress. The horses no longer could pull the wagon. Eph unhitched his team. Putting the supplies on the back of the roan and saddling the bay horse, he was prepared for any eventuality. He rode along the ridges which were blown clear of the snow. On and on he hurried, on past Devil's Gate and down toward Sweetwater River.

The intensified blizzard obliterated the roadway for Eph. Bewildered, he zigzagged some distance from the bare ridge road he had been following. Making his way slowly, he rode into a small Indian encampment on the fringe of scrub timber. These Indians did not know Eph and were not friendly to the lone Mormon rescuer. He was not invited to warm himself before their fire. Suspiciously and enviously, they circled around him and his horses. They coveted his handsome horses and outfit.

Eph explained in a guttural voice, "Me lost way. Me need hurry to find people pulling handcarts. Show me road."

Big Hawk, chief of the Indians, shook his head, "Me see white man pull handcart before snow, but they all be dead now. Snow bad!"

Some of the braves pointed east and said, "There road. You find." Eph dismounted and, pulling his hunting knife from his boot, scratched lines in the snow, showing the Indians that he was well acquainted with the area and knew well the road in good weather. Intentionally he left his knife on the snow, continued to talk to the Indians, and then mounted his bay horse. From the corner of his eye he observed one of the Indians kick snow over his knife and stand on it.

Indicating his satisfaction with their directions, he pulled the reins of the mount's bridle and rode off a short distance. The Indians watched him closely. Eph suddenly stopped his horse and felt in his boot for the hunting knife. He searched his boot, his coat, and the saddle, and looked around his pack horse. "Huh! no knife." He rode back to the Indians.

Eph raised his hands high above his head and began to pray, half in Indian dialect and half in English, to the Great Spirit. Drawing his eyes into narrow slits, he pointed straight to the feet of the Indian standing on his knife. "Which one you got my knife?" he queried. The Indians shook their heads. "Me no got knife," each responded.

Eph looked upward and again talked to the Great Spirit. Then Eph pointed directly at the guilty brave who stood trembling in his moccasins. "You stand on my knife! Give to me." The Indian bent over, picked up the snow-covered knife, and handed it to Eph.

With his knife retrieved and the Indians deeply impressed with his magical influence with the Great Spirit, Eph said, "Big Chief, you send two men, guide me to road." Immediately two were appointed. Yet in the blinding blizzard, they too were confused and led Eph in the wrong direction. The storm abated some and Eph recognized familiar landmarks. He excused his guides, giving them a handful of dried fruit, and rode on his way alone.

Just before dark Eph camped for the night in a deep narrow gorge. As he cleared away the snow to make his bed, he thought, "How comfortable it would be to have a buffalo robe to cover me while I sleep, and I'd surely relish some buffalo meat for supper." He was instinctively led to ask the Lord to send him a buffalo. He had scarcely ended his prayer when he looked around and spotted a buffalo bull within fifty yards of where he stood. Surprised beyond expression, he soon calmed his feelings and, with his first shot, brought down the big buffalo. He spread the hide on the snow and placed his blanket upon it. He ate the tongue and other choice parts of the animal. He had a refreshing night's sleep, and his horses browsed on the sagebrush.

The next morning he cut up the meat in long strips and loaded them onto his horses. He struggled all day through the storm. The sun was setting when in the distance ahead Eph saw a black streak in the snow. Getting nearer, he observed that it moved. He had at last arrived at the ill-fated Martin Handcart Company.

The pitiful sight that caught his gaze as he entered the camp Eph could never erase from his memory. Shivering in the snow, several hundred starved figures with haggard countenances trudged slowly about trying to prepare a scanty evening meal.

The handcart pioneers were snowed in on the Sweetwater River, unable to move. They had almost no food and were hundreds of miles from any source of supplies. Death was frequent. The survivors were too weak to dig graves to bury the dead. Among the suffering handcart people were George Read and his wife, Elizabeth, who were converted to the restored gospel in London, England. They were the parents of two daughters, Alicia and Thisbe, and one son, Walter. A few days before the handcart company had arrived at Omaha, Nebraska, eight-year-old Walter had strayed from the encampment. A thorough search was undertaken, but he could not be found.

The suffering of the stranded Saints had become so intense that many doubted if help could reach them before they would all be dead. Then came the joyful afternoon when, before dusk, they saw a dark spot moving toward them. Thisbe Read, as did all the other suffering handcart people, thanked the Lord for the strong man who had brought them fresh hope and meat to eat. As the years passed, Thisbe's admiration for Eph increased.

As Eph rode in among them, they flocked around him with expressions of thanks and praise to their God. One after another would plead, "Oh, please give me a small piece of meat." "My poor children are starving;

do give me a little." In five minutes both of his horses were relieved of the extra burden of buffalo meat. The people in the camp were soon busily cooking and eating with grateful hearts.

The snowstorm had overtaken these brave suffering handcart Saints as they reached the Sweetwater River. There they had settled down in the freezing blizzard to await help or die, being unable to go any farther. It was here in this utter extremity that the courageous Eph came with the first relief, as the man in the gray tweeds had invited him to do.

The suffering condition of the handcart people almost melted Eph's heart. He rose in his saddle and spoke cheering and comforting words to them. He assured them that they should all have the privilege of riding into the Salt Lake Valley as more teams were on their way to them.

Eph was a unique character, observed one of the handcart men. He was lithe as an Indian and clad in buckskin from his head to his feet. On his head he wore, pushed back, a broad-brimmed hat; and below the rim strands of his light hair extended. His ruddy face, reddened by exposure to the wind and frost, and his easy manners made him a picture all eyes riveted on.

That evening around a blazing fire, Eph joined the group, dragging the bushy buffalo tail of the bison he had slaughtered and brought to the starving people. Reaching the fire, he sprang on the end of the logs and, swinging the tail around his head, shouted a "Hoop! Hoopla! Hoopee!" and threw it into the fire between the burning timbers. He picked up a small limb. Facing the interested group, he pulled out his pocketknife and commenced whittling off the twigs from the bough. He confidently said to his new acquaintances, "Pretty darned cold nights now, boys, and none too much warmer the day time—never mind—perk up. Them teams will soon reach yer, and they'll bring some flour and bacon with 'em too." Still whittling —"When them teams get here, we'll stack them blame carts and jest get fer the valley. Yer see, yer ain't used to this kinda life. It don't hurt me—I'm kinder used to it. If I can only get my cayuse under shelter, I kin roll up in a buffalo skin and sleep snug enough. A strip of jerked beef will do me fer days."

Being intrigued by Eph's language, the listeners had forgotten all about the buffalo tail. He had whittled a sharp ended stick and with it he poked the fire until he pierced the tail. Bringing it out smoking hot, the hair burned off, he held it on the stick until it cooled enough to handle. He held the roasted tail at both ends and tore off bits of the meat with his teeth with a relish which caused all the onlookers, who had just had their fill, to smile broadly. They forgot their sadness, and the sunlight of hope lighted their tired and weary souls.

After dark that evening, a woman, crying aloud, passed the fire before which sat Eph. She implored Daniel Tyler to come and administer to her husband who was nigh unto death. Tyler, tired, weak, and weary had just retired for the night. Reluctantly, he arose and followed the woman to the tent in which he found what appeared to him to be the lifeless form of her husband. He said, "I cannot administer to a dead man." Eph had walked with Tyler and the sorrow-stricken woman to where her husband lay. After Tyler returned to his resting place, Eph walked back to the campfire around which four of the brethren were sitting. "Will you boys do just as I tell you?" The answer was in the affirmative. They warmed water over the fire and together washed the body of the dying man. Eph anointed his body with consecrated oil. Together the men laid their hands upon his head, and Eph commanded him in the name of Jesus Christ to breathe and live.

The effect was instantaneous. The man, who was dead to all outward appearances, began to breathe. He sat up in bed and sang a hymn. His wife, unable to control her joy and thankfulness, ran through the camp, uttering excitedly, "My husband was dead but is now alive. Praised be the name of God. The man who brought the buffalo meat has healed him!"

This remarkable incident created gladness in the whole camp. Many drooping spirits took fresh courage. From then on, Eph's time, when not hunting buffalo, was given to waiting on the sick. Pleas from those whose dear ones were sorely afflicted came to him: "Come with me, help me!" "Please administer to my sick wife!" "Come, please, my child is dying!" Eph spent days going from tent to tent administering to the sick. As Eph recalled, "The result of our labor of love certainly rebounded to the honor and glory of a kind and merciful God." Eph administered to scores every day. Many of their lives were saved by the power of God.

One evening he was requested by a woman to administer to her son, Thomas. He had been sick for a number of days and was not expected to live. On the hard ground bed where he lay, he was moaning pitifully, too weak to turn his body. Eph felt the power of God resting mightily upon him. He bent over and whispered in the boy's ear, "Will you believe the words I tell you?" His feeble response was, "Yes." Eph blessed him, and he arose completely healed. He got up from his bed, dressed himself, and danced a hornpipe on the end board of a wagon.

Many of the handcart Saints whose extremities were frozen, lost their limbs, either whole or in part. Eph washed them with water and castile soap until the frozen parts pulled off, after which he severed the shreds of flesh from the remaining portions of their limbs with scissors. One little girl lost both her legs below the knees on her tenth birthday. She was Nellie Unthank. Her parents had died before Eph arrived. As he removed the stockings from her feet, some of the flesh from her feet and legs was pulled off with the stockings. To save her life she was strapped to a board, and without antiseptic her feet were cut off with a knife and a carpenter's saw. Years later Nellie married, raised six children, took in washing, and kept an immaculate house but was never free from pain. This noble handcart pioneer really lived. She gave the world more than she received, yet felt that she was blessed. Her life story inspires and strengthens and is a monument to the gospel of Jesus Christ. She held Eph Hanks in grateful remembrance. Surely no part of the great exodus west is more touching and fraught with heroism and courage, mingled with pain and tragedy, than the handcart pioneers.

The relief teams met the handcart immigrants and brought them into the Salt Lake Valley. Around the campfires at night the teamsters were told of the hunting skills and healing powers possessed by Eph. They seemed to them impossible. No man could do what the handcart people attributed to Eph Hanks. While they were sitting around the evening fire, smiling and somewhat questioning the truth of Eph's prowess, a bird flew over the heads of the men where Eph was frying some buffalo meat. Eph threw his butcher knife into the air and struck the bird; it fell near the frying pan. This adroit act confirmed the stories told about Eph, leaving no doubt in their minds.

A few days after this, Eph and his friend, George, who had come with the rescue teams, rode out to hunt a buffalo for the immigrants. They spotted a herd grazing on a hillside. They crept stealthily within rifle range of it. George shot at a big bull and wounded it. Then it charged at George, bellowing and snorting. He took careful aim at the attacking bison, but his gun misfired, so he took to his heels and ran. George felt the hot, frothy breath of the buffalo on his legs. He spotted a clump of brush and leaped into it. The buffalo plunged into the brush, his horns barely missing George. The buffalo stood bellowing, pawing up the dirt, and then sullenly ambled back to join the herd. Eph laughed to see George run like a deer to escape the young buffalo, but he had his rifle ready to shoot the bull were it necessary.

By the time the Martin Handcart Company reached South Pass, enough relief teams had arrived to make the journey more rapid. The strength and spirit of the handcart Saints was revived when the supply wagons arrived, but by the time they reached Fort Bridger the supplies again ran low. Tom Dobson, a teenager, recalled how Eph made possible the replenishment of needed meat.

They had eaten the last of their food. The wagons formed a circle for the night. One old lady had carried with her a bantam rooster in a box. After the fire was lighted, Eph said, "Granny, get your rooster and let 'im run around the fire to crow." Indians had gathered with the Mormons around the warm fire. They had never seen a tame chicken, and the little bantam rooster was a curiosity. The Indians were so intrigued that they brought their chief to see and hear the rooster crow.

Eph traded the rooster to the Indians for two steers and two ponies. The steers were butchered. That night the starving immigrants enjoyed a delicious dinner. Tom, as an old man, affirmed, "That immigrant party owed its life to Eph Hanks."

Eph was a rough mountaineer, but at heart he was gentle, of a sympathetic nature, and a man with great faith in God. His resourcefulness and effectiveness in administering to and caring for the frost-bitten handcart people endeared him to hundreds who benefited from his services.

Soon the relief wagons numbered one hundred and four and the immigrants reached the mouth of Emigration Canyon. After escorting the handcart company to the Valley, Eph galloped into Salt Lake City on his bay steed and stopped at the "Old Tabernacle" as the

Sunday morning services were in progress.

Upon hearing of the approach of the handcart people, President Young dismissed the congregation with this counsel:

"When those persons arrive I want to have them distributed in this city among the families that have good, comfortable houses. I wish the sisters before me and all who know how, to nurse and wait upon the newcomers, and prudently administer medicine and food to them. Prayer is good, but when baked potatoes and pudding and milk are needed, prayer will not supply their place. Now that our handcart saints are here, we will continue our labors of love until they are able to take care of themselves, and we will receive the blessing."

The heroic efforts of Eph Hanks and the other brave men who bore the trying and adventurous burden of rescuing the storm-bound and starving handcart immigrants were highly praised by President Brigham Young. "They put works to our faith; they realized that our faith alone would have been perfectly dead and useless, would have been of no avail in saving our brethren that were in the snow. By putting works with faith, we have been blessed in rescuing many and bringing them here to the valley."

If courage and endurance make a chapter in the life of Eph Hanks, if human kindness and brotherly love in the midst of horror are worth remembering, Eph's heroic part in the rescue of the handcart immigrants will be recorded in the annals of eternity, and Eph will be there to read it.

# 7

# PIONEER MAIL CARRIER

Farming was too boring for Eph. He craved action and adventure, riding over the plains, and encounters with Indians. He had not consulted Harriet, who enjoyed their simple life in their new adobe farm home which she had furnished and arranged so comfortably for pioneer times, when he had contracted to carry mail from Salt Lake City to the Missouri River. In this means of livelihood, he would be in congenial surroundings. During the next seven years, he would make the thousand-mile trip fifty times and enjoy each one of them.

Telling Harriet of his intentions was difficult. He entered the front room which Harriet had stocked to the ceiling with good foods. Rows of hams and sausage of all shapes, and rows of fruits preserved with honey, marmalade, and jam filled the room. He stood enchanted, breathing in the delightful atmosphere. "Why should I leave all this?" he breathed with a sigh. He called, "Harriet, I'm home." His tones died away in the stillness. He walked out the door and around the house, and there she was, hoeing the garden he had planted for her. He thought, "She shouldn't do this in her pregnant condition."

Walking up behind her, he wrapped her supple body into his arms. She gasped in startled surprise. Seeing her husband, she whispered smilingly, "Oh, it's you, Eph. You frightened me. Why are you home so early from your farm work?"

Eph's broad shoulders were slightly bent, his long hair thick and blond, and his ruddy, still clean-shaven face, set off by clear blue eyes. Harriet's tall, handsome husband of twenty-five years was tense with emotion he must unloose to convey to her his contract to carry the mail for the next seven years. But he did get it out, surprisingly, and didn't bungle it. She stood, now out from his arms, a pillar of coolness, bearing the disturbing news like ice. A thousand feelings rushed on Harriet. Eph watched her expressions, her tenseness. He was somewhat consoled now the telling was over. Moments seemed eternity before Harriet looked up into the blue eyes of her husband and said, "If that's your desire, Eph, I will support you and be with you in spirit all through your journeys. You've no doubt asked Sidney to take care of the farm?" She was ahead of him as she always seemed to be and ever would be.

He kissed her tenderly, "You're a jewel, Harriet! The

money I'll earn in carrying the mail will make your adobe house into a mansion."

"Eph, I don't want a mansion—all I've ever wanted was to have you near me each day—but—" and her sobbing words trailed off as Eph held her close to him.

Eph, with Feramorz Little and Charles Decker as partners, had made the mail contract with S. H. Woodson. The first trip east with the mail was made by Eph and Little in mid-July. Beyond the continental divide they met a company en route to California. The old man posing as wagon master irritably conveyed to them in short sentences that the Bannock Indians appeared hostile near Red Buttes. He was troubled with his responsibility as the boss of the little group going to California to make their fortune. He could not, so he said, turn away from his involvement with the quarrelsome men pushing westward to the gold streams. "I doubt the damn Mormons will let us through their city!" he grumbled.

"Ah, shucks, old man, those Mormons won't anymore than scald the hide off ya in their hot springs. You'll get by. Drive on!" encouraged Eph with a chuckle.

Eph and Little drove on until late afternoon and stopped at Willow Springs. Here they unharnessed their horses and staked them out to graze. They made the usual preparations for camping through the night to deceive any Indians who perchance might be watching their movements. They kindled a blazing fire, then slipped out into the shadows, harnessed their horses, and drove on to the Red Buttes, stopped their wagon on the road, hobbled their horses, and, making no fire to reveal their presence, spread their blankets behind the wagon, crawled in, and slept soundly throughout the night. The next morning they saw the paw prints of a huge grizzly bear within a foot of the spot where their heads had been resting on the blankets. They were grateful for having slept so soundly that not a muscle twitched to disclose them to the big grizzly.

Each trip to the Missouri River and return to Salt Lake City took forty to fifty days. One dreadful winter, Eph and Little spent almost a month in a cave with their horses to escape a long snowstorm. Men and animals survived on jerked meat rolled in flour during those tedious, wearisome days in the cave. The hazardous winter journeys exacted a heavy toll on strength and courage. The government paid them one thousand dollars a trip, and they earned every penny of it.

One day in early August, Eph and Charley Decker were assigned to take the Honorable John M. Bernhisel, the first representative of the Territory of Utah to the Congress of the United States, through to the Missouri River so that he would reach Washington for the opening session of Congress. Bernhisel was a highly refined and cultured gentleman from Pennsylvania and was politically a Whig. Eph and Charley were Democratic mail carriers. Their outfit consisted of a light wagon drawn by two mules, three pack horses loaded with government mail, and two of Eph's saddle horses.

Doctor Bernhisel enjoyed the ride over the mountainous country until they stopped before the upper crossing of the North Platte River. The river moved slowly. It seemed sluggish. The surface lay flat. Birds circled lazily overhead. But there was no ferryboat to take them across to the east bank where the old pioneer trail continued southward toward the Missouri River.

Anticipating such a situation, Eph had put in the back of the light wagon four ten-gallon kegs. Loading the mail from the backs of the pack horses into the wagon, Eph and Charley, having unhitched the mules, pushed the wagon into the river, lashed a keg to each wheel, and tied a long rope to the wagon tongue. Holding the rope, Eph swam to the other bank of the North Platte, while Charley rode and led the horses and mules across to the east side of the sluggish stream.

Then, how to get Utah's first congressman over? He was a poor swimmer, if he could swim at all. It was too much of a risk to have him in the light wagon. Eph and Charley swam back to where the nervous doctor stood. They fastened the rope securely under his arms. Wading out into the river, the two young mail carriers pulled Bernhisel along through the water. His Whig political inclinations they were fully aware of. Reaching the main channel, the men were separated; it was then every fellow for himself. Eph and Charley let go of the doctor, who yelled frantically for help. "Don't let me drown! I'm your representative to Congress!" Eph made it to shore still having the end of the lengthy rope in his hand. On land he tied the end of the rope to the saddle horn and leaped on his fiery steed. The honorable congressman, resembling a fluttering hippo, was pulled headlong through the sluggish, slow moving river at rapid speed to the east bank. He was almost suffocated by submersion in the muddy stream, but Eph and Charley worked him over and they all moved on down the pioneer trail. Eph and Charley had muscular spasms caused by their laughter when they read in the *Frontier Guardian*, a Mormon paper printed in Council Bluffs, Iowa, a letter from Dr. Bernhisel, dated from Independence, Missouri. He wrote: "I arrived here this afternoon in good health. Should you deem it worthy to notice please say in the *Guardian* that I am neutral in politics."

Returning from the Missouri River with the mail from the east, Eph and Charley exhausted their provisions. They saw camped along the Sweetwater River a company of gold-seekers who were by reputation over-stocked with food. When they rode into the gold-seekers' camp and asked to purchase supplies, the haughty wagon boss curtly refused to sell them anything. Riding back to their wagon, they drove out of sight of the gold-seekers' encampment.

Eph, with a twinkle in his eye, said to Charley, "Let's you and I give 'em a whirl." Charley's black eyes flashed; his Roman nose twitched with pleasure. "What've you got in mind, Eph?"

"With plenty of feathers, horse hair, charcoal, and paint, Charley, we can make you a full-fledged Indian chief of the most savage order."

These young mail carriers spoke the Indian dialect fluently and had crossed the plains so many times they knew each blade of grass. They were not going to be outdone by a camp of tenderfoot miners.

Everything was made ready. Eph rode one way, Charley the other. The make-believe Indian chief galloped up a deep ravine that led a distance from the gold-seekers' camp. Both men were mounted on good horses and were heavily armed. Eph, in the buckskin garb of a mountaineer, followed the river bottom, keeping out of sight until he reached the main road a half mile west of the gold-seekers' camp. Reversing his course, he followed a trail leading to their wagons. He rode into the camp and excitedly informed the men that they were in a hotbed of bloodthirsty Indians whose delight was to peel the scalps from the heads of unwary travelers who trespassed on their lands.

The gold-seekers were roused to a frenzy. Then over the hillside, galloping on his cayuse, came Charley, yelling and swinging his gun in wild and threatening gestures. He harangued the shocked westward travelers in genuine Indian language, swinging his arms and pointing to the mountains, the hills, and the plains.

The excited tobacco-chewing humans gathered around Eph's horse. With a flush of emotion and apprehension, they earnestly inquired of Eph what the "damned redskin" was gabbing about.

"Men, I know Indian talk so I'll ask the old chief what the matter is," said Eph.

After talking to the "chief," he walked up to the exasperated wagon boss and said with feigned concern, "Captain, he wants you to understand that he and his people own this whole country as far as your eye can see and that you will have to pay dearly for the rich bunchgrass your hungry animals have devoured during the last five sleeps, or one of you, maybe heap more, will lose your scalps, just as sure as his name is Sitting Bull."

The captain, wet with the sweat of fearful apprehension, inquired of Eph what the damages were. They were more than willing to pay rather than be molested by a band of cold-blooded savages.

After the "chief" and the "mountaineer" conversed in a spirited talk, Eph told the wagon captain, "The chief says he wants bacon, beans, coffee, sugar, tobacco, and flour to make biscuits." The wagon boss ordered the commissary to bring out the demanded supplies. "Chief" Charley commenced to jabber again, at the same time rubbing his stomach and making horrid faces. The wagon captain asked Eph, "What's the old cuss kicking about this time?"

Good naturedly Eph explained that the chief's wife was very sick and he wanted some brandy to rub on her stomach as well as candy for his papooses.

Clear of the camp, Eph and Charley soon rejoined and rode to their own camp a mile or so down the road. They chuckled to themselves, and Eph congratulated Charley on his superb acting ability. In the gold-seekers' camp the captain and his men congratulated themselves on the clever manner in which they had saved themselves from Indian disaster.

In mid-December, 1856, Eph and Feramorz Little, after a blessing from President Brigham Young and his counselors, left Salt Lake City with pack and saddle animals to carry the mail to the Missouri River. Eph had assured his Harriet that she need not worry because the Prophet's blessing would secure him and Little from danger and he'd return safely. He kissed her and their two little children goodbye. Her eyes followed Eph out the door and up to the gate where his saddle horse was tied. She heard his voice call out a last goodbye, and then horse and rider disappeared.

When they turned to look from the top of Big Mountain on the valley below, Eph and Feramorz thought the snow and the heavy drifts formed by cold gusty winds might prove too much for their experience and endurance. "Will we see home again?" asked Little.

"God will determine that," replied Eph. "Let's ride on."

Taking the more barren ridges as the snow had drifted into the valleys, they arrived at Devil's Gate on Christmas Eve. Here they met a few brethren left to guard goods and cattle left behind by handcart companies.

Christmas morning the two mail carriers left Devil's Gate. During the day after Christmas a snow storm fell. Soon the roads were obliterated. Eph decided to camp before they lost all direction. Through the blinding snow, they saw a small grove of timber and soon reached it without difficulty. As they entered the enclosure, they heard a dog bark. "There must be an Indian camp near," said Eph. Riding on in the direction where they had heard the bark of the dog, they came upon a young Indian. Eph asked him to direct them to the lodge of the chief.

Stopping before the lodge, they were greeted by

Old Smoke, a Sioux chief with whom Eph was well acquainted. Eph and Feramorz sat astride their mounts until Chief Old Smoke invited them to dismount. They entered the lodge. Fifteen warriors gathered around them. Chief Old Smoke grunted to his squaw, "Get white men food, heap quick." She and her older papooses soon had biscuits, coffee, and fresh meat ready for her husband's guests. The pipe of peace was smoked by Indians and whites after the dinner.

The weather continued cold and the snow remained deep. Progress was slow. Often after a tedious and strenuous day's travel for both animals and men, they had scarcely gotten out of sight of the previous night's camp. A few green cottonwood trees along the river furnished a little forage for the hungry animals. To obtain fuel, Eph traveled along the bluff of the Platte River, mostly uncovered with snow. There he found small sticks and pieces of dry bark. Filling his big pockets, he deposited them in an empty pack and gathered more. He generally gathered over a bushel of sticks and bark which made for them a warm fire at night and over which they cooked their food.

Numerous buffalo along the snow-covered plains supplied Eph and Little with fresh meat. The choicest parts were cut for their meals. Wolves in ravenous bands followed the mail carriers and devoured the remainders of the buffalo carcasses left by Eph and Feramorz. These rapacious and greedy canine critters barked in sharp, loud howls. Always famished, they were voraciously excited by the smell of blood. Exceedingly fierce and quarrelsome, they fought among themselves. Following the mail carriers day after day they often came too close for comfort. Eph would then fire his revolver which frightened them away. If the shot drew blood, the pack pounced upon the wounded wolf and devoured it.

After a buffalo was killed and the hunters had cut from the carcass the choice parts and had turned their back upon the kill, the snarling, snapping, growling pack rushed upon the remains, and in an instant almost nothing was left but bones.

Within twelve miles of Ash Hollow, Eph and Little overtook John Snead and Old Phil. They informed the mail carriers that the two Indian traders, Major Dips and Mr. Mechat, on their journey back from the Missouri River after purchasing yearly supplies, had been overtaken by severe snowstorms at Ash Hollow, one hundred and fifty miles east of Laramie. The snowstorms were so severe and the temperature below zero for so long that their cattle died rapidly from starvation. The two traders hired John Snead and Old Phil and provided them with a suitable outfit of ponies to ride back to Laramie for one hundred head of fresh cattle. Of the animals they had purchased for the traders at Laramie all had died except five poor oxen which they were driving when Eph and Little overtook them. These two men had subsisted on the miserable meat cut from the exhausted oxen. With the five remaining they hoped to reach Ash Hollow.

The mail carriers saw two wretched-looking men— lean, emaciated, hollow eyed. Poor diet, laborious travel, and exposure to cold would soon bring upon them the same fate as their exhausted animals left strewn along the now-covered trail. Mr. Snead told Eph that for several days he dreaded to walk ahead of Old Phil on the trail for fear the Indian would kill and eat him. Good food was furnished them by the mail carriers, and in two days they reached Ash Hollow.

When Eph and his bosom companion, Feramorz Little, reached Ash Hollow they were surprised to find eight of Major and Russell's transport company's freight teams snowed in. The wagons were loaded with mail for the East. A Mr. Remick was the head wagoner. The teams were distraught and full of uncertainty since their food supply was nearly exhausted. Eph cheered them with the assurance that they would reach the Missouri River. "I'll furnish you with all the buffalo meat you and your men can eat while you make the journey to the Missouri," Eph told Remick.

A large band of Cheyenne Indians was camped a short distance from Ash Hollow. Eph felt impressed to visit them. He rode in the deep snow to the camp and went directly to the chief's tent. An elderly female was sitting on the far side from the entrance. In a moment the chief entered with a group of braves. The chief inquired, "Who are you? Where you come from?"

In the language of the Cheyenne, Eph replied, "I live in mountains. My people pulled handcarts across plains. My chief, Brigham Young, talks with Great Spirit."

The chief eagerly asked, "You talk to Great Spirit?" Eph smilingly answered, "Yes, I talk to Great Spirit."

The chief spoke to two assembled warriors who left the lodge and returned in a few moments, carrying an Indian boy in a blanket. The invalid boy was the chief's son. Months before on a buffalo hunt with his father, he was thrown from the horse he was riding. His back was badly injured, and since that unfortunate accident he had been unable to move.

The chief, pointing to his son on the blanket asked, "You talk to Great Spirit for my son?" Eph solemnly consented. He ordered the two braves to remove the clothing from the boy's body, and then he anointed the injured back and limbs with consecrated oil which he always had with him and sealed the anointing in the name of Jesus Christ, promising the boy that he would be made whole from that very moment. The boy immediately rose from the blanket and walked out of the lodge to the astonishment of the chief and his braves.

Eph informed the chief that a company of freighters at Ash Hollow were nearly out of provisions. "Could you help starving palefaces with buffalo meat?"

The chief said, "No buffalo here for moons. My people starve—no can spare meat. Too bad—me like to."

The spirit of prophecy came upon Eph in a remarkable degree. He said, "Chief and braves, I promise you in name of Great Spirit that within three suns whole county be overrun with buffalo." This prediction caused a stir of surprise among the braves who looked at their chief questioningly. The chief smiled and nodded to Eph, "We believe." Eph bade the Indians goodbye and rode to the Remick camp but said nothing about where he had been.

Next morning, as Eph, Feramorz, Remick, and the

wagoners were getting ready to start on a six-hundred-mile journey toward the rising sun, thirty Indian braves formed two lines on each side of the snow-covered roadway. As Eph passed in the lead wagon, each brave gave him a package of the choicest kind of sausage made from buffalo meat which was recognized by the Remick outfit as a godsend to them all. The Indians anxiously inquired, "When will paleface who talks to Great Spirit come back to us?" Eph informed them he would return in two moons and would come to their village. Tears trickled down the dusky cheeks of the braves when Eph gave each one a parting shake of the hand and bade each of them farewell.

Little and Remick inquired of Eph what this generous giving of buffalo sausage meant to them. This was the first time they had ever known Indians to give away food, especially in times of famine. Eph replied, "I have always been kind to the redmen of the plains, and they are a people who never overlook a kind act."

One night soon after leaving Ash Hollow, Eph dreamed that his company had all the buffalo meat they could take care of, and even their mules and horses joined them in the feast. The next morning when he predicted they would have buffalo meat to spare and that even the mules would eat fresh meat, Remick and his teamsters ridiculed him. As the day wore on and they traveled in the fallen snow they continued to taunt Eph who took their abuse good naturedly but repeated his prediction.

That evening as he chose a place to camp for the night near a stream, Eph spotted a big buffalo up the stream a hundred yards. After shooting the bison and dragging it to the campsite, he was dressing it when the teams pulling the wagons drove up. The men couldn't believe their eyes. They sheepishly admitted that part of Eph's prediction had been fulfilled but scoffed at the idea that mules would eat buffalo meat.

After Eph had cut choice parts of the bison, the cook filled a large camp kettle with fresh meat. He mixed plenty of flour with the small pieces. The campfire crackled and put out much heat while the kettle boiled briskly, but the cook failed to watch the pot, and the meat burned. The camp cook's ill nature boiled over the burnt stew, and in a fit of anger he dumped the contents of the kettle onto the ground a few yards away from the fire. Without too much apology for his rash act, the cook got another pot of meat boiling. The hungry animals strolled into camp and, smelling the flour on the burned meat, they rushed for it, the mules gulping down the meat and flour to the amazement of the teamsters. Eph smiled.

Two days later, Eph informed the men that they would cross a river that afternoon. "If you do as I tell you, you will not get wet." "What is that, Mr. Wizard?" asked Remick, thinking that Eph intended to play some practical joke upon them. A short travel brought the teamsters to the banks of a wide frozen-over river. As Remick in the lead wagon started driving over the ice, Eph called to him, "Stop, Remick! Go no farther!" But Remick, taking the call as a joke, cracked the whip over the backs of his mules. He had not gone far when crack! the ice broke, and down went his wagon and mules in the icy water up to the wagon bed. Remick and several of his teamsters were drenched before they reached the opposite bank. "I'll be damned, Hanks, if you ain't some prophet," blustered the wet and shivering team master.

Within twenty-five miles of Fort Kearney in the Nebraska territory, Captain Remick good-naturedly inquired, "What next, Mr. Prophet?"

"You will ride into Fort Kearney blindfolded," replied Eph.

"Will I get sick?" anxiously inquired Remick.

"No; you will simply ride into the fort blindfolded."

The next day the sun shone so brightly that Captain Remick and a number of his teamsters were snow blinded. So intense was the pain that the men bandaged their eyes.

The commanding officers at Fort Kearney precisely informed Captain Remick that to travel farther in the heavy snow with the mail was impossible. "You'll need to tarry at the fort several days until the deep snow melts before you can get through."

Remick declared, "We can go through all right. We are being piloted by a man who can take us anywhere."

The officer waved his hands as he said, "Very well, Captain. If that is so, go ahead, and we will furnish you with such things as you need."

With Eph as their pilot, the wagon train moved onward and eastward in snow two feet deep. They arrived in Independence, Missouri, January 7, 1857, Eph and Feramorz having been on the road from Salt Lake City just twenty-eight days.

In Independence, Eph and Feramorz were dumb-founded to find the air filled with rumors of war, and government agents arriving who were preparing to march against the Mormons. They had, according to Judge Drummond's untruthful stories, destroyed the court records in Utah and were in open rebellion against the United States Government.

Feramorz Little penned and signed a letter to the *New York Herald* which was published on April 15, 1957. It read:

"As myself and Mr. E. K. Hanks are the last persons who have come to the States from Great Salt Lake City, I deem it my duty to bear testimony against the lying scribblers who seem to be doing their utmost to stir up a bad feeling against the Mormons. We left our homes on the 11th of December, brought the last mail to the States, and certainly should know the state of things there. The charges of Judge Drummond are as false as he is corrupt. Before I left for the States, I was five days every week in Great Salt Lake City, and I witness to all the world that I never heard one word of the burning of nine hundred volumes of law records, etc., nor anything of that character."

Eph and Feramorz separated in Independence. Eph returned with the mail ready to take west, while Feramorz waited two weeks for the next mail shipment to arrive from the East. With the mail Eph camped one night on the east bank of the Platte River. Cold winds made it necessary for him to find shelter in a little cove near the stream. He unpacked and hobbled his mules, gathered wood, and knelt to light a fire. Above him on the high part of the riverbank, he saw Sioux Indians approaching—war paint, arrows, and tomahawks all ready to take Eph's scalp. Leaving all else, Eph put the box of matches in the crown of his hat and his hunting knife in the scabbard inside his boot. He grabbed a strong willow hanging over the water and swung himself under the bank into the river. He swam quietly under the bank for a ways downstream and paddled across the river. Here he rested, cold and shivering, until darkness hid him from his savage pursuers. He slept in the bottom of a buffalo trail worn deep by the herds of bison.

At dawn the buffalo trailed to the river for water. With his long hunting knife tied to a sapling he cut the hamstrings of a big bull, skinned the animal, and roasted enough meat over the fire to sustain him for a few days. After two days of walking, he located the Indian camp on the other side of the Platte River. The Sioux had taken his horses, the mail, his revolver, and the mules. The night of his second day of searching, Eph swam quietly across the river and located the band of horses and the Indian night-herder. Eph's low whistle brought his faithful horse from the band to his side, and then they were gone, leading the other horses with them.

When the sun arose the next morning, Eph had the band of Indian horses on the opposite side of the river, herding them on a knoll in full view of the Indians. The Indians brought his saddle, guns, mail, and all the things they had taken, piled them on the bank of the river, and then retreated to their camp, beckoning Eph to cross over the river. He crossed with his horse and mules, took his saddles, mail and equipment, and then drove the Indian horses across to their camp.

Eph followed the trail west over the top of a mountain which sloped into a little valley. Not far away as he entered the valley, Sioux Indians were dancing a war dance. They saw him. There was no way for him to escape, so he rode directly to the chief's wickiup where he was surrounded by yelling, howling savages. He dismounted. Without restraining their loud, doleful howling, the Indians grabbed his horses, saddles, the mail bags, and equipment, piece by piece.

Eph strode into the chief's tepee. On the blanket in the back corner lay an Indian boy, the chief's son, who had moments before been thrown from a pony and had been trampled on by a buffalo herd. His back was seriously injured, and he was in severe pain. He could not move. Hanks spoke to the chief. He understood the Sioux language. The chief pointed to the helpless boy, "You white medicine man make my boy well. We let you go."

Eph stepped over to the boy, bent downward, and placed his hands on the Indian's head. Fervently he implored the God of Heaven to heal the injured Indian boy. His prayer was answered. In moments, the chief's son arose from the blanket and walked about the camp. The grateful chief roared a boisterous command, savages darted hither and thither, and in minutes the purloined prizes snatched from Eph were reassembled, and Eph started on his way with the blessings of the Indians.

When Eph arrived at Ash Hollow, the mountaineers in that vicinity asked him what he had done
for the Indians to create such a stir among them. The
Cheyennes had been inquiring about him for the last
month. Eph asked the mountaineers if they had seen
any buffalo in those parts since he left there in January.
"Yes, about three days after you left, one of the biggest
herds of bison that has been seen in this part of the
country for a long time passed by here, and they were
just in time to save us from starvation as our food supply was nearly gone."

The moment Eph made his appearance among the
Ash Hollow Indians, the news spread like wildfire, and
the whole tribe hurried out to meet the man who healed and prophesied for their good.

Warring braves wept for joy;
The women danced with gladness.
Shouts from redskins rent the air,
That banished care and sadness.

Halfway from the Missouri River on the Laramie
Bottoms, Eph met a company of Mormons with thir-
teen wagons. Besides missionaries going east, there was
the family of Moses Davis who was taking a large herd
of livestock to market in Missouri. Albert Davis, a young
man of twenty-four years, recognized Eph and invited
him to spend the evening and night with them. After
preparing camp for the night, Davis—with several other
young men—was watering the herd at a little spring.
Suddenly a band of Indians rode out of ambush,
whooping and riding into the drinking cattle, intending

to stampede them. Eph mounted his horse and galloped to assist Davis and the other men.

Riding and yelling back and forth behind the frightened cattle, they succeeded in driving them on a dead run toward camp. Six of the Indians rode into the herd and tried to turn the cattle away from the camp. With two navy revolvers Albert Davis fired steadily at the Indians, forcing them to ride away from the stampeding herd.

As they got the cattle safely into the enclosed wagon camp ring, one of the camp members shouted, "The Indians are riding pell-mell down the hollow!" Eph, Albert, and the other young Mormon men on their mounts, bravely rode out to meet the advancing Indians. A fierce exchange of lead and arrows occurred before the Mormon boys succeeded in driving the warriors away. One brave rode close to the whites and deliberately fell off his pony onto the ground. After driving the attackers away, Eph dismounted and walked over to the fallen red man. He turned the Indian over as he had fallen on his stomach with his face on the ground, and exclaimed: "Men, this is no Indian—he's a young white man!" He had been slightly wounded by a bullet grazing his shoulder.

Eph helped the young man to his feet. "Who are you, boy?"

"I am Walter Reed. Some years ago I was with the Mormon handcart people. One morning I wandered away from camp and was taken by the Sioux Indians. Are you Mormons?"

"Yes, we are Mormons," replied Eph, "and I'm on

my way to Salt Lake City. I'll take you with me, and you'll join your family in a few days."

Seven of the Mormon men were wounded. A young Dane, John Svenson, was wounded with two arrows in his left arm. Another Mormon named Peter was overtaken on foot by the Indians. They surrounded him, but he was swift of foot and sprinted between their horses and streaked for camp. The Indians galloped after him, shooting arrows at the fleeing white man. He reached camp and fell exhausted on the ground. One arrow with an iron spike had pierced his cheek and clinched deep in the cheek bone. Another arrow had gone clear through his neck, fortunately missing vital spots.

With Eph and Miles Romney as principal surgeons, each wounded man sat down on a wagon hub and gripped the spokes. Their only surgical instrument consisted of the blacksmith's pincers. Romney succeeded in pulling the arrow shaft loose from the iron spike which was firmly lodged in Peter's cheekbone. Eph said, "Miles, I have a pair of pincers with extra long handles. We can pluck the iron spike out with them." He soon had the pincers. The man sat on an ox yoke. Romney and Davis held Peter's head firmly, and Eph got a firm grip on the iron spike and succeeded in pulling it out. Peter arose from the yoke and in broken English mumbled, "Tank you! Tank you."

Eph proceeded west as far as Bear River with the eastern mail. Here he joined with a small group of men en route to the Salt Lake Valley. Reaching the Weber River, they boarded a raft. The river was a swollen, foaming torrent of water. A short distance from the east bank, the raft was sucked under, forcing Eph and the men with him to swim for their lives. The mail Eph was carrying to the valley was carried down the stream and lay in the water for two hours. After an arduous search and at the risk of his life, Eph secured the mail, but it was in bad condition. Eph's clothes were drenched, and he had no recourse but to wrap himself in robes and blankets, wet as water could make them, until morning. He was then freely perspiring, fully relieved from the fever he had been laboring under most of the time since he left the wagon company. That day he continued his journey and reached home late in the night.

# 8

## THE EXPLOITS OF EPH HANKS

One lovely autumn day, after Eph had delivered a wagonload of fish he had caught from Utah Lake to his customers in Salt Lake City, he drove down an infrequently traveled street lined with maple trees luxuriantly covered with vermillion leaves. In between the trees grew goldenrod delicately tinted; overhead a flock of geese sailed by. About the foothills, the haze of autumn covered the horizon. He breathed the crisp air and uttered, "It's good to be alive." Then he recalled the difficulties the Saints had endured with the Government appointees sent to the Utah territory. There was Associate Justice Perry E. Brocchus, a vain, ambitious, immoral, revengeful hypocrite, who lectured the Mormons on morality and virtue and insulted Eph and the other Saints with his insinuations. Then the Saints received two honest, upright men in Lazarus H. Reed, whose father Eph had known, and Leonidas Shaver. Shaver was straightforward and judicious, but he died suddenly in the night after three years as Associate Justice of the territory. Eph held to the saddle horn and grimaced; then came Bill Drummond, a bully and gambler who was a disgrace to the administration at Washington. He brought with him Ada Carroll, the wife of a Baltimore school teacher. He was never married to her, and this licentious and open adulterer had protested against the practice of polygamy in the territory. Levi Abrahams, a Jew who ran a shop, and a convert to Mormonism, made a slighting remark about Drummond and the mistress he had brought with him from Washington, D.C. It made the justice angry, and he swore revenge. Eph lifted his eyes from his meditation on past happenings to see Cato, the Negro servant of Drummond, horsewhipping Levi Abrahams. Eph stopped his team of horses, pulled on the brake, and leaped from the high seat of his wagon. In two giant leaps he grabbed the horsewhip out of Cato's black paw and flung it away from his reach. Grabbing the Negro by the nape of the neck, he jerked him from the stunned and bleeding Jew.

"You degenerate descendant of Ham, why in God's name are you whipping poor, little, defenseless Brother Abrahams?"

"White trash, take yo' hand off me—I ain't no descendant from no ol' Ham. I'se descendant of Niggardemus!"

"Who set you on this man?" demanded Eph.

"My master, Judge Drummond, he done to'e me to whip hell out of this damn Jew."

"Nigger, had I my hands on the honorable Drummond I'd rub his dirty nose in the blood you've drawn by your horsewhip from Brother Abrahams." With that Eph shoved the Negro flat on his face just as a crowd of excited men rushed on the scene. On his feet in an instant, Cato fled to the Drummond quarters. Levi Abraham's bleeding body was cared for.

Drummond and Cato were arrested for assault and battery with intent to murder; but through an agreement that the judge would leave the Utah Territory and not return, the case was dropped. He left for Carson Valley where it was presumed he'd hold court, but he hurried on to California with his courtesan. From there he went to Washington, D.C., by way of Panama, spoiling for revenge. With lies and misrepresentations, he proved a damaging witness to the Saints in Utah.

On reaching the nation's capital, Drummond resigned and submitted to the United States attorney general charges against the Mormons which caused him to declare that the Mormons were in open rebellion against the United States government. Drummond alleged that Brigham Young was absolute dictator in Utah, that Mormon men were bound to him by secret oaths and set apart as destroying angels to take the life and property of those who questioned Brigham Young's authority. He said that the Federal officials were insulted, harassed, and annoyed by the Mormons and that Brigham Young had destroyed the court records.

Drummond blamed the Mormons for the murders of Captain John W. Gunnison and Almon W. Babbitt. (Both were killed by Indians.) He also said the Mormons poisoned his predecessor, Judge Leonidas Shaver. This was ridiculous, as Gunnison and Shaver were favorites of the Saints, and Babbitt, Secretary of the Territory, was a loyal member of the Church. Because of previous prevarications reported against the Mormons, Federal officials had concluded that an expedition should be sent to Utah, but Drummond's report added fuel to the fire and served to speed the disciplinary action to be taken against the Church.

Prior to the Civil War, polygamy was politically linked with the slavery issue. Slavery and polygamy became a campaign issue in 1856. The Republican platform called for the elimination of the "twin relics of barbarism—polygamy and slavery." James Buchanan and the Democrats won on the popular sovereignty doctrine, defeating John C. Fremont and the "twin relics" issue. After becoming president, Buchanan stood his ground on slavery but reversed himself on the polygamy question. He resorted to the prevailing belief that the Mormons had challenged the authority of the United States government. Without investigation after Drummond's report, he took the stand that the issue was not polygamy but rebellion. Through his military chief, General Winfield Scott, Buchanan ordered John B. Floyd, Secretary of War and later one of the leaders in the rebellion over slavery, to send 2,600 troops to Utah under General W. S. Harney of Fort Leavenworth. Harney had been active in punishing the Sioux Indians along the immigrant trail and was notoriously called the "squaw killer." Harney was later replaced as commander by Colonel Albert Sidney Johnston, who was strong on punishing the Mormons on the practice of polygamy but who three years later left his post to join the southern rebellion and died for the slavery issue.

Rumors leaked through to Utah about Harney's assignment, but definite news did not reach the saints until July 24, 1857, when three thousand people were having a picnic in one of the canyons, celebrating their first ten years in the valleys of the mountains.

Utah Territory defense militia retained the name of the Nauvoo Legion and had a standing strength of two thousand able-bodied men between the ages of eighteen and forty-five. This army was led by Lieutenant General Daniel H. Wells. On August 1, 1857 he informed the Legion that Utah was about to be "invaded by a hostile force." He knew of no reason for sending an army against a people who stood for the Constitution and against mob rule; therefore, every legion member was to prepare to defend the homeland.

Political expediency dictated that Senator Stephen A. Douglas win the support of the populace by a scathing denunciation of the Mormons. Therefore, in a major political address made by Senator Stephen A. Douglas, in Springfield, Illinois, an erstwhile friend of the Saints while they lived in Illinois, he referred to the Mormons in Utah as a cancer in the body politic and said, "The knife must be applied to this pestiferous disgusting cancer which is gnawing into the very vitals of the body politic. It must be let out by the roots and seared over by the red-hot iron of stern, unflinching law." He charged that nine out of every ten of Utah's inhabitants were aliens and illiterate and were bound to their leader by "horrid oaths," that the Church was inciting the Indians to acts of hostility, and that the Danites or "Destroying Angels" were robbing and killing American citizens.

The rumors and reports mentioned by Douglas were not new, but it was new for the Saints to hear such talk from a man who had befriended them. They reminded Douglas that the Prophet Joseph Smith had told him he would aspire for the presidency of the United States; but if he ever raised his voice against the Mormons the hand of God would rest heavily upon him, and he would fail to reach the presidency.

Governor Brigham Young of the Utah Territory and other Church officials planned to defend Zion and halt the advancing military. The leaders engendered in the Saints confidence that the Lord who had led them to the valleys of the mountains would protect them against military encroachments.

This was the theme of one Mormon war song:

> If Uncle Sam's determined
> On his very foolish plan,
> The Lord will fight our battles
> And we'll help him if we can.

While the Mormons were hastening their defense, a messenger from General Harney was on his way to Salt Lake City. He was Captain Stewart Van Vliet, who was traveling with a small detachment. Coming through the canyon into the valley, he stopped at

Eph Hanks's ranch at Mountain Dell, and Eph, learning of his mission, accompanied him with the offer to
introduce him to Governor Brigham Young. This was
Eph's first knowledge that the president of the United
States was sending an army to Utah.

In the presence of Governor Young, the messenger
from General Harney was tactful and assured the Mormon leaders that the soldiers were sent on a peaceful
mission and that they would pay liberal prices for all
supplies needed. But Brigham Young, his counselors,
and the Twelve Apostles said bluntly they didn't want
the army to enter the Great Salt Lake Valley. Yet Captain Van Vliet was given the opportunity to speak to
the Saints in a public meeting on September 13, and
President Young introduced him as a man of honor for
whom soldiers had respect. The captain could give no
assurances regarding the conduct of the army. He made
it clear that the army would come and that resistance
would be futile. He was told if the army entered the
valley of the Saints they would find a scorched earth.
The Saints would devastate everything they had built
or planted or anything they had made attractive
through their industry, before abandoning it to the
enemy.

In the meeting, Elder John Taylor of the Council
of the Twelve, put this question to the congregation:
"All of you that are willing to set fire to your property
and lay it in ashes rather than submit to their military
rule and oppression manifest it by raising your hands."
All hands went up accompanied by a loud, "Amen!"

The day following the public meeting, Van Vliet left Salt Lake City. Two days later at Green River he wrote his report. He reported the Mormons expected the worst from the army, believing the coming of the soldiers would be the beginning of such persecutions as they had experienced in Missouri and Illinois. He believed the Saints would resist to the last man and were capable of stiff opposition. But his superiors did not take the report seriously.

Hosea Stout, a formidable participant in this conflict, wrote in his journal: "Captain Van Vliet tried to dissuade the troops from coming into Utah but without effect. The first regiment, when they found they would be opposed, raised a shout and threw up their hats and said they would have some fun now that the Mormons had spunk enough to fight."

Governor Young called Eph and his friend, William Kimball, into his office and requested them to ride posthaste to Carson Valley with orders for the settlers there to come home. Within three weeks the families had sold out, and about 450 persons with 123 wagons were en route for Salt Lake Valley. Of this number 160 were capable of bearing arms. These brethren brought from California 2,700 pounds of ammunition and many firearms. Eph and William acquired two braces of pistols of the latest caliber and strapped them to their belts. The entire San Bernardino colony of over one thousand Saints migrated. Most of them located in Southern Utah.

Eph and William spent the one night they were in Carson Valley in a tavern and witnessed an interesting episode in the saloon portion of the tavern. Gold had recently been found, and the tavern was full of miners.

As Eph and William sat munching their evening meal, there walked into the saloon a tall, lank westerner dressed in the best broadcloth suit, a freshly starched white shirt, a brightly colored necktie, a Stetson ten-gallon hat, and fancy cowboy boots. He was conspicuously out of place among the rough, coarsely attired miners. He was eyed by all in the room. One of his old comrades asked, "John, where did you get such fancy clothes? How can you afford such?"

John replied, "I can afford to wear these fancy clothes because they cost me nothing." Gasps of unbelief sounded throughout the room, and the bartender dropped a mug in surprise.

"How did this happen?" a chorus of voices inquired.

Long John smilingly, but seriously, replied, "Because Joseph Smith was a true prophet."

"What has that to do with your getting that suit of clothes?" incredulously asked the bartender.

"Gather around, boys, and I'll tell you." Almost every man left his table and crowded around the well-dressed man. "I went into a store in Carson that an old friend of mine kept. I was dead broke and had on next to nothing, and the storekeeper asked me why I didn't wear better clothes. I told him I'd like to." Long John continued, "My friend, the store owner, told me to pick out the best suit I could find in the store and pay him when Stephen A. Douglas was elected President." At that time almost the entire nation was sure

Douglas would be its next president. "Well, fellows, I picked out this suit and then told my friend I'd take two suits on them terms, but he said one was all he proposed to let me have."

The men in the bar asked him how he dared take the suit on those terms as they were sure he'd have to pay for them even though he had no steady work and mining was a shaky way to get money. John smiled and explained. "You see, Joseph Smith told Douglas years ago, before Douglas ever thought of trying to be president, that he would try for it someday, and if he used his influence against the Mormons he should never sit in the president's chair. I kept watch and kept thinking of that prophecy jest to see if Smith was a true prophet. When I saw Douglas trying to be President next election, I knew Joseph Smith was a true prophet and that Douglas would not be elected because he turned against the Mormons. I have watched Smith's prophecies and have never seen one of them fail."

Eph and William walked up to tall John and invited him to sit at their table. Eph said, "My friend, we were impressed with what you said about Joseph Smith's prophecies. Both of us knew Joseph Smith, and we know he is a true prophet of God. We are Mormons from Utah." John was flabbergasted and stammered, "You fellows are Mormons? Well, I'll be damned. I never thought I'd ever meet a Mormon. This suit I owe to Joseph Smith. Do you live in Carson Valley?"

"No, we live in Salt Lake Valley. We are here to take the Mormons out of Carson Valley back to Utah to help us defend our lives and property against an invasion of the government army sent by President Buchanan to put down a supposed rebellion. This action was partly brought about by Douglas's speech against us at Springfield, Illinois."

"Yeah, I heard of it when he came out against you Mormons. That speech will cost him the presidency."

"Indeed it will," concurred Eph. "We have sent him by letter and in our newspaper, *The Deseret News*, reminders of the Prophet Joseph's prophecy about him and that he'll never reach the president's chair."

"And you knew Joseph Smith?" anxiously asked John.

"We certainly did. He died a martyr for his religion."

"I'd like to have known him," mused John, and then he spoke up with eager enthusiasm. "I'm going with you Mormon boys and help you fight the U.S. troops."

"You'll be welcome, Long John."

"My name is John Silverton, and I'm from New Jersey. Ain't had no luck at mining, but I could be a good Mormon."

On the 15th of September, Governor Brigham Young issued his famous proclamation, declaring the Territory of Utah under martial law. He forbade all armed forces of any description from coming into the territory under any pretense whatever. He called for all forces of the territory to hold themselves in readiness to march at a moment's notice to repel any and all such invasion. "No person shall be allowed to pass or repass into, or through, or from this Territory, without a permit from the proper officer."

The day after Governor Young's proclamation, Eph

and William with John arrived in Salt Lake City and reported to the president that the Carson Valley Saints were on their way to Utah. They introduced John Silverton to the governor of Utah Territory, who welcomed him to Zion.

John was amazed at the calmness, the confidence, and the assurance of the Mormons over the coming of government troops against them. He heard Jesse Earl's experiences when he stayed overnight in a camp of the U.S. troops. Earl said, "They were marching on, very unconcerned and deliberate, not dreaming trouble but anticipating fine times in Salt Lake Valley this winter while walking over . . . our people, hanging up our rulers and prostituting our women."

John ground his teeth in anger and mumbled fiercely to Eph and William, "Let's get organized and go out and stop those damned intruders before they get any closer." Eph and William knew they had a confirmed convert with them.

Eph thought of the physical hardships and sacrifices he and the other pioneers had endured to conquer and subdue the western wilderness. "We are more than colonizers," he mused. "We are, above all, Saints of Almighty God. We sacrificed for a divine purpose; we represent a great cause; our physical endurance is but tributary to it. We fled from oppression which took the lives of our Prophet and Patriarch and which burned the roofs over our heads and destroyed our crops in the field. But we'll never suffer such to happen to us again. Rather than break the covenant we made with our God we would rather die, but He will fight our battles. We are not afraid." Then out of his bosom followed the prayer, "O God, give me strength to help defend the cause of Zion and to stop the soldiers in their tracks." Eph Hanks was prepared and ready!

Toward the end of September, General Daniel H. Wells took the field to direct the defense. Legionnaires were ordered to annoy the enemy without spilling blood or risking their own lives. Provisions were removed from the Mormon immigrant storehouse called Fort Supply. They were prepared to burn all the buildings or improvements which could be used by the incoming soldiers. Several families left Fort Supply for Salt Lake City.

Eph Hanks and his companions rode to the fort to help take care of the crops and make ready to burn everything if it were necessary. He, with the families still living at Fort Supply, took out horses, wagons, wheat, flour, and other foodstuff, and at high noon set fire to the buildings, consisting of one hundred or more good hewn houses, a saw mill, a grist mill, and one threshing machine. Going out of the fort, they set fire to the stockade. Many of the owners begged for the privilege of setting fire to their own property, destroying at once without a sign of regret what they had spent years to build. Long John couldn't believe what he saw and marveled at the sacrifice the Saints so willingly made rather than leave it to the approaching army.

Lieutenant General Daniel H. Wells and staff established headquarters at Fort Bridger, which the

Mormons had purchased a few years before from the mountain man, Jim Bridger. From here he carried out the orders sent him from Governor Brigham Young. Here he devised means of harassment to delay the army without coming in actual conflict with it. Major Lot Smith was sent out with fifty men to stampede the animals and set fire to the army's supply trains. Colonel Robert T. Burton and a company of men were dispatched to burn the country before and on the sides of the approaching army, to destroy the fords at the rivers, and to blockade roads by felling trees across them. Eph Hanks with Howard Eagen, Porter Rockwell, and others were sent as scouts to observe the army at all times and keep communications open. Governor Young instructed General Wells, "Save life always if it is possible. We do not wish to shed one drop of blood if it can be avoided. This course will give us great influence abroad." Governor Young ordered that Fort Bridger be destroyed as it was in the path of the enemy, and it was burned.

Eph Hanks and the others named above were called the Be'boys and often alluded to as "Brigham's Boys." Perhaps no subordinate military man took a more important part in the Utah War than Eph Hanks. So daring was he in some of his exploits that the bravest of the Be'boys were not anxious to follow him on his reconnoitering expeditions. One dark night he crawled so near the officers' tent that the cook unknowingly threw scraps from the colonel's table over him. On another dark night, Eph crawled near the army encampment. The cook had a huge pot of coffee boiling over a camp fire near a clump of willows not far from the dining area. When the coffee was ready to be poured for the officers' supper, Eph cut a forked willow, hooked it into the bail of the pot, and hoisted the coffee into the brush. This liquid was served by Eph to his fellow scouts for their supper. Nothing occurred at the officers' headquarters that he was not aware of. He kept General Wells posted on every important movement made by Johnston's army. (For Sidney Johnston had recently arrived to take command.) Eph captured a number of Uncle Sam's teams and drove them into the legionnaires' encampments, which hindered considerably the troops' attempts to enter the Salt Lake Valley the fall of 1857.

From one of his eavesdropping missions on the officers' headquarters, he learned they intended stirring up the Snake and Shoshone Indians to fight the Mormons. Knowing the Indian chiefs of these tribes, he took his friend, William Kimball, and rode into the Snake and Shoshone country to meet with them. They rode two fine horses they had run off from the army and traveled till about midnight when they stopped at a mountain stream. Here, across the creek, they saw Indian fires a distance from them. They tied their mounts to the birch trees and waded up the stream. Their belts were hung with the colt revolvers they had been given in Carson Valley. They lay on the bank of the stream. Two white men captured by the Snake Indians—stripped of their clothing, their hands and feet tied—were lying before the fire while the savages danced around them and amused themselves by thrusting brands of fire on their naked bodies.

Witnessing this revolting scene for a moment or two, Eph and William opened fire with revolvers in each of their hands, and as soon as those were emptied they each picked up another pair and continued firing at the fleeing Indians. Being taken by such sudden surprise, the Indians fled without their guns, leaving their prisoners. Eph and his companion unbound the men, secured their clothing, guns, and horses, and sped into the night.

The men identified themselves as teamsters with the army supply wagons. They had ridden from their encampment when the redskins grabbed them. Eph suggested that William ride back with the teamsters and get them safely to their wagons then ride on to General Wells and report to him what Eph was doing.

Eph loved excitement and danger—qualities that gave him great influence with the Indians. He was, by nature, an athlete of tremendous agility, strength, and vitality. He spent weeks among the hostile Indians of the plains. He visited one tribe after another; and in this way, by intelligent diplomacy, he was instrumental in dissuading the Indians from joining with the incoming army; a decision which saved many lives. His contacts with the chiefs of the prairie redskins reflected his love for all God's children.

Eph knew the Indians so intimately that he met them either in peace talks or, if necessary, in battle. Eph spoke the language the Indians understood best.

One day after dark, Eph rode into a Snake Indian village. The braves on the alert stopped him but, knowing him, directed his way to the chief's tepee. Coming to the flap on the front of the tepee, Eph stopped. He could hear the old chief, bent and wrinkled, humming the song dear to Eph and the Saints—William Clayton's "Come, Come, Ye Saints."

The aged chief looked up and, seeing Eph, arose, invited him to enter, greeted him warmly, and offered Eph some venison. As Eph ate the meat he asked, "Chief Big Horn, when did you learn the Mormon marching song, 'Come, Come, Ye Saints'?"

Chief Big Horn smiled, "I tell. Many, many moons ago my people were on the war path. We hated the palefaces. We held council and decided to kill all palefaces. A company of palefaces were going west. It was almost to Rocky Mountains. I was chief of thousand braves. That night we waited silently on the mountain pass for palefaces led by big chief Brigham Young. My braves had bows and arrows behind every rock, waiting for signal from me to attack palefaces.

"The palefaces camped for night. Their campfires burned brightly and the palefaces danced and sang. Then, around camp fires they sang 'Come, Come, Ye Saints.'

"I gave signal, but braves' fingers like stone; not one arrow shot. Braves and me, the chief, mount cayuses and ride away. We know Great Spirit watching over palefaces.

"Eph, my friend, this is my song. It is your song, my song every night before I lay down in tepee. Song brings Great Spirit to me, makes me and my people happy."

Chief Big Horn assured Eph that the Snake Indians

would not war against Mormons. "Mormons our friend; Brigham Young, big paleface chief, my friend. Mericats come—we no like. We help Mormons drive Mericats away."

Eph spent the night in the old chief's tepee. He lay on the floor but hardly slept a wink. The wind blew fiercely; the night was black as the grave. Not a star nor a glimmer of moonshine slipped through the canopy of the clouds. For some unknown reason, Eph felt apprehensive about something. His feelings were much as they had been the year before when the voice of the man in the tweed suit called to him in the early morning, "Eph, those handcart people need you."

Early the next morning, Eph bade Chief Big Horn a good day and, with strips of jerky in his pocket, started his ride back to the Echo Canyon encampment of the legionnaires. The air was cold and disagreeable. Snow flurries commenced to encircle him as he sped southwestward. Before he reached the road traveled by emigrants, a veritable blizzard of wind and snow enveloped Eph, and he let the horse find the way. Over a hill along the stream of icy water, Eph came suddenly upon a company of stranded, helpless handcart Mormons, struggling in the blizzard, not knowing what to do.

This was the second of two handcart companies of 1857 to make an anxious march, getting to Utah ahead of the advance unit of Johnston's army. Would this second company make it? William E. Waters, an officer in Johnston's army, noted that in the company, now snowbound, the wagons were used only to carry baggage and rations and could not accommodate even those who were sick. They had no tents nor protection from the storm. Eph observed the sad sight. The road was lined with handcart Saints, laboring to get along in this severe snowstorm. Old and decrepit men and women, some with wooden shoes, some with canvas bottoms sewed to their stockings, others without any foot coverings, were tottering along at the rear of the slow-moving ox teams. But slow as they moved, it was too fast for some of them. Not withstanding all this hardship, murmuring was not heard.

When Eph arrived upon the struggling handcart Saints, they rejoiced to see him. Besides being weary and distraught, they were hungry. The day before the sudden snowstorm, an old man, devoid of the sense of smell, was walking some distance from the handcart when he saw an animal that might be suitable for food. Creeping noiselessly upon the animal he whacked it fiercely with his cane until it was lifeless. Throwing the little striped beast over his shoulder, he walked proudly to the handcart caravan. As he approached, all the men, women, and children retreated. The man's gift was vociferously declined; even the giver of the skunk was unbearable. With no change of clothing available, the well-meaning man was ostracized.

Eph gathered the suffering Saints around him and instructed them how to scrape away the snow and make a comfortable encampment. He assured them that the sudden snowstorm would abate, that he'd have some buffalo meat for them within the hour, and that on the morrow rescue wagons would be there. Once again Eph proved to be a savior of a stricken people, and their sad countenances brightened as they gathered around the brisk warm fires lit by their benefactor. He observed that the carts were tastefully painted to suit the fancy of their owners with inscriptions on the sides. One was inscribed, "Truth Will Prevail." Others in bright paint read, "Zion's Express," "Blessings Follow Sacrifice" and "Merry Mormons." Two teenage girls showed Eph their cart with "Blessings Follow Sacrifice" and said, "Today in this cold blizzard when we began to feel sorry for ourselves we pointed to these words and comforted each other with, 'We'll soon count our blessings and forget this experience in the snow.'" Around the warm campfires they proved to Eph they *were* Merry Mormons, pushing Zion's Express.

Eph further comforted them with the assurance that the United Sates army camped on the Green River would not harm the Saints of God. "You'll see that our God will fight our battles. You have nothing to fear. Keep before you the vision of Zion in the mountains and your part in the full establishment of it. Always have faith in this lofty goal and hold on to the rugged course of attaining it. Our Lord Jesus Christ endured the cross for the joy that was set before Him."

Soberly they heard Eph Hanks and smiled with assurance and comfort as they unitedly exclaimed, "God bless you, Brother Hanks. God sent you to us."

A few rods ahead of the handcart company, Eph spotted the tracks of two buffalo and followed them. Further down where the snow was smooth, he followed the tracks out of the main valley and up a small, tight, hollow that lay boxed in by two low steep hills. The wind came down the broad valley at his back, so Eph circled the hill on the right of the hollow so he would be downwind from the buffaloes. He scanned the hollow below him. His penetrating gaze rested upon a stand of saplings, and there was the shaggy side of one of the buffaloes. Eph tethered his horse to a tree and walked in the soft snow around the hill, keeping the bulge of the hill between him and buffalo. He reached a clump of willows which afforded concealment and then, taking careful aim, he slowly pressed the trigger of his rifle. Bam! There was a flash of fire and a billow of dark smoke. The sharp report of the rifle bounced in the air, and mingled with it came the loud, terror-stricken bellow of the great bull. The other buffalo bolted in fright and charged down the hollow. Eph ran to the fallen bison crumpled in the snow and rolled it on its side. With his sharp hunting knife Eph slit its throat. Then, tying his lariat rope around its two forelegs, he wrapped the other end of the rope to the horn of his saddle, mounted the army mustang, and touched its sides with his spurs.

The newlyfallen snow made the pulling of the huge carcass rather easy; and, as the route to the handcart encampment was downward, within the hour he was there amidst the shouting of the hungry, grateful handcart Saints.

After dressing the buffalo and cutting it into many choice cuts for the gathering immigrants, Eph gave the warm furry hide to a family of shivering youngsters. "Wrap yourselves in this warm robe and you'll never be cold again," cheerfully invited Eph.

That evening, as young and old were gratefully devouring the buffalo meat, over and over Eph heard individuals exclaiming, "That's mighty tasty eating!" They crowded around the fires for hours, roasting meat and warming themselves, but Eph rode on to the Echo Canyon fortifications. The next day he talked with Hosea Stout, Preston Thomas, and other Nauvoo Legionnaires stationed at Echo Canyon where they had built formidable fortifications on the tops of the cliffs which would conceal one thousand men who could pour a deadly fire on Johnston's army were he to attempt to enter the canyon on his way to Salt Lake City. Hearing from Eph the plight of the handcart company, these men hitched teams to nine wagons and drove to the encampment, taking bedding and food. Within a week they had assisted the handcart people to reach Salt Lake Valley.

The early snowfall was a Godsend for the defenders of Zion. There was no attempt on the part of Johnston's army to enter Salt Lake Valley during the winter. When the army went into winter quarters at Camp Scott on the Green River, the campaign of the Utah War was closed. It ended without the legionnaires firing a single shot at the U.S. Army. Surely the Lord had fought his people's battle as Eph had foretold.

In April, 1858, Alfred Cumming, the newly appointed Governor of Utah Territory who was camped with the army at Camp Scott, was persuaded by Colonel Thomas L. Kane to visit Brigham Young in Salt Lake City for a peace conference. Little did these two dignitaries know that before reaching the valley they would be safely protected in their journey by Eph Hanks and the boys. According to plans, the dignitaries left Camp Scott with two carriages. They traveled fifteen miles, upset one of the carriages in the snow and were obliged to stay in this upset condition for the night. The next morning Eph Hanks, William Kimball, John Kay, Howard Eagen, and Porter Rockwell, who were out scouting in the vicinity, righted the upset carriage and escorted the governor, Colonel Kane, and party safely into the Salt Lake Valley.

# 9

# FIREWATER—NO GOOD

Volumes could not contain all the heroic deeds performed by the remarkable Eph Hanks. Prophet Brigham spoke of his virtues. Once he said, "There is not a man who has been as ready to lay down his life for the General Authorities, the Church, and for the cause of Zion and the Saints as Eph." He was the means of helping to make it possible for thousands of immigrants to get to the Salt Lake Valley and dwell in peace in the mountain vastness. The Indians learned to respect him. His influence among them was remarkable. No Mormon had more ascendancy with them than he had. Naturally, Eph was intelligent, God fearing, and liberal to a fault. Habitually cheerful, rarely did he utter a word of complaint.

Now he was home for a spell. Harriet and the

children were overjoyed. As Harriet was preparing a bounteous meal to celebrate his return, she good-naturedly said to her husband, "Now, Eph Hanks, you get over to that wash basin and shear off that bushy beard and shave your face smooth or you won't get a bite to eat. You're as hairy as the buffalo on the plains. But, oh, you're adorable! We're so glad to have you home. You are staying for awhile?"

"Yes, Harriet. I'm working the farm and taking care of you and the children. No one but you could get me to cut off my wavy beard."

"The Prophet got you to shave it off some years ago," retorted his wife.

The children tugged at Eph's trousers and coaxed him to take them in his arms. After shaving, he held them on his lap. They said, "We like your face smooth. Before you shaved we kissed Mama kinda slow, for Mama's face is soft but you we kissed quickly 'cause your face was prickly." Eph laughed and hugged his children. "That's worth the shave," he smiled.

"Daddy, tell us a story about the handcart people."

Eph was an entertaining storyteller. That evening with his wife and children around him was memorable to the king of the Mormon scouts.

Spring burst with the color of fresh vegetation. The cow pasture was aglow with sego lilies, butter cups, and dog-tooth violets. Eph and Jack, his hired man, busied themselves cleaning out the irrigation ditch and getting the water onto his freshly planted spring grain.

Jack bantered with Eph. "So Harriet had you cut off your beard?"

"Yeah, a clean-faced husband is part of her religion."

"Speaking of religion," commented Jack, "since you've been gone, Brother Brigham has made the Word of Wisdom a commandment—no longer 'not by restraint.' One thing I can't understand is why all the good things are reserved for the Gentiles."

"You still tap the whiskey jug, Jack?"

"Yeah—have to for my stomach's sake, and I get headaches."

"Balderdash," laughed Eph, "it's not for your stomach's sake, Jack."

"Seriously, Eph. I guess my religious convictions are about as shallow as the Danish brother who spoke in church Sunday."

"What did he say?" inquired Eph.

"He said, 'Brothers and Sisters, when I cross the plains, my vagon vheel, she squeak and she squeak. I go to Bruder Brigham, and I say, 'My vagon vheel, she squeak and she squeak.' And Bruder Brigham say, 'Bruder Yohnson, put a little grease on de vagon vheel and she no squeak.' So I put grease on de vagon vheel and she squeak no more. Now, I know the gospel here am true.' "

Eph chuckled but then added, "Now that spring has come you better cut drinking firewater with the Indians."

Eph discovered a large break in the irrigation ditch made by a burrowing gopher. He called for Jack, and together they labored feverishly to mend the break. After hours of futile effort, Eph and Jack were about to give up when "Old Harelip," an Indian who had camped on the hillside above Eph's field, sauntered to where the men were laboring. He slouched over to see what was happening. He took one look at the rupture in the ditch and called to his squaw. From the wigwam came the reply, "Tow winee! Tow winee! Amou yah!"

Again Harelip shouted, and from the wigwam lumbered a squaw of ponderous proportion. Harelip gave a command, but his squaw furiously protested. Finally she flung herself into the stream and filled the gap. Eph and Jack piled the sod against Sally's great bulk, and within ten minutes the break was repaired. The grateful Eph said to Harelip, "Wino squaw."

Later that day, Harriet worried as she rocked the crib to get the baby asleep. She glanced anxiously at the open door. There was Jack milling around the barn. She said to her oldest son, Brad, six years of age, "I wish your father would come."

"Where is my faver?"

"In town on business," Harriet sighed.

The little six-year-old, Brad, stole out of the house to greet Jack at the barn. He ran to the house very excitedly and said, "Mom, Jack gave me some burning stuff out of a bottle."

Alarmed, Harriet tried to think of a way to get the bottle of whiskey from Jack. Were the Indians to get a taste of this firewater, there would be no way to restrain their hostile tendancies; she knew the ways of the Indians. Harriet knew old Chief Tabby and his braves would be coming again to beg for biscuits and sugar. She had fed them before.

Harriet prepared the evening meal of ham, eggs,

warmed-over potatoes, steamed bread, and milk. Responding to her call, Jack trotted into the house without stopping to wash his face or hands. He sat down at the table and called, "Boy, come and bless this hash."

The six-year-old lad stepped to the table and blessed the food. After finishing the dinner, he patted the boy on the head. "You're a good Mormon boy." Drinking a second glass of milk, Harriet inquired of Jack about the bottle of whiskey.

"Oh," stammered Jack, "Tarman passed by, and I bought it. I had a bad headache."

"Did it cure your headache?"

"Yes, pretty good."

"If your headache is cured, give me the bottle. Old Chief Tabby will come soon to beg. He will find us without Eph. If he gets a smell of that firewater, he'll become dangerous."

"I'll blow his head off if he starts acting funny," blustered Jack.

"Jack, you know the Prophet Brigham warned us about exciting the Indians with threats," sternly declared Harriet. "Be wise—I have four little children."

"Don't worry." Jack said confidently. "When it comes to Injuns, I know how to use a gun."

"Listen, Jack, you keep your gun out of use—were you to harm one Indian, the rest of us would be slaughtered."

While his mother cautioned Jack about the use of firearms when Indians came to beg, Brad's mind worked busily. He remembered where Jack had hidden the whiskey bottle in the barn under some straw. Slipping out the kitchen door, he scampered to the barn, snatched the bottle from under the straw, scurried to the back door of the log house, and called to his mother.

While Jack was eating his second piece of apple pie, Harriet walked into the bedroom, took the bottle handed her by Brad, and poured the whiskey out the bedroom window. Returning to the kitchen, she gave Jack an old quilt. "You're tired. Go out and lie down on this quilt under the apple tree on the south side of the barn."

Jack refused her offer. "I'd rather lie on the hay in the barn." He pushed back the chair and started for the door. He reached above the door for Eph's gun. "I'll kill the first damn Indian that steps on the Hanks's property."

Harriet caught Jack's arm. "Now, Jack," she said firmly, "Leave the gun here. I'll feed the Indians if they come."

As Jack hesitated on the front steps, he put on his hat and slowly mumbled, "All right, if you want to feed 'em, go ahead. But them redskins ain't gonna get a drop on me!"

Staring over the horizon he said with harshness, "Did you know the damn Injuns killed my father two years ago on the Oregon trail? I'm not taking any chances with them red devils." Ending his saying, Jack sauntered down to the barn.

Little Brad said to his mother, "If he gets mad, Mother, I'll take the blame."

"Don't worry, son," Harriet said softly as she

cuddled her oldest boy in her arms. "I feel safe now, even if Jack gets mad."

As the hired man opened the door and disappeared into the barn, three Indians galloped into sight on their sorrel cayuses. Harriet and Brad knelt on the living room floor and pleaded with their Heavenly Father for His protection.

Failing to find his whiskey, Jack pushed open the barn door and saw the three Indians dismount and walk briskly to the house. He likewise walked rapidly and reached the front steps when Chief Tabby and his two braves arrived. Harriet came to the door. "Me want biscuit. Me hungry," grunted Chief Tabby.

Harriet said, "I will bring you biscuit."

Chief Tabby got a whiff of Jack's whiskey-scented breath—he knew firewater was nearby. To Jack he begged, "Give me firewater. Heap sick—me heap sick. Firewater."

Jack swore and ordered, "Keep your nose out of my face or I'll smash yours in."

Harriet hurriedly explained, "Chief Tabby, white man sick. He drank firewater all gone."

Old Chief Tabby grabbed the bottle, held it to his mouth and sucked out the last remaining drop. He smacked his lips, "Heap good—want more." He scowled at Jack and grunted to his braves.

They shoved Jack to the side and rushed into the house to search for firewater. One brave walked to the cradle and scowled down at the sleeping infant, feeling the edge of his hunting knife. Harriet edged near the crib and pushed the Indian away, her heart pounding. Jack, emboldened by the whiskey and angered at the disrespectful treatment given him by the Indians, snatched the fire shovel at the edge of the fireplace and struck the Indian nearest the crib on the head. The brave fell to the floor. Jack sprang for the gun over the door. Harriet was alert and seized Jack's arm. Pulling with all her strength, she screamed, "Red men, get out of the house quickly! Vamoose!"

Chief Tabby stopped his search for firewater and said to the Indian near him, "White man and squaw crazy. Go out—crazy!" The two red men helped the brave up from the floor, dragged him hurriedly out to where their horses were tethered, and pushed him onto his cayuse; and the three of them galloped away.

# 10

# THE IRON HORSE

"Reckon that ought to do for this time," Eph grunted to himself after hammering the last nail on a lean-to Harriet requested he attach to the ranch house. Eph shook his head, tossing back a mane of hair beginning to gray. He threw out his arms and slowly raised them in a long refreshing stretch, which tended to rid him of the cramps of his labor. For a few moments he inspected the results of his toil and was about to walk into the house and invite Harriet to view the finished addition, when down the road he saw a cloud of dust.

Amidst the rising, dry pulverized particles of earth he saw a band of mustangs driven by two Arapahoe Indians. One of the Indians rode speedily in front of the wild cayuses and succeeded in stopping them in front of the Hanks's ranch house. Eph recognized the redskin to be To-sharpooe or White Eye. Walking to the high board gate, Eph called out, "White Eye, where did you get all those mavericks?"

"Friend Eph, me get them off high ranges. Iron Horse scare cayuses off grazing land. They put tails in air and run like coyotes. Bearfoot and me round them up. Like to buy some? We sell cheap to white friend Eph," shouted White Eye.

"You say Iron Horse frightened these horses and they ran onto Arapahoe land?" asked Eph.

"Yes, scare like rabbits. We get—we sell you some."

"What is this Iron Horse?" inquired Eph. Bearfoot was having trouble keeping the horses together, so Eph told the Indians to run the band into the corral, and he opened the high board gate.

"Iron Horse big, black, no got legs—has wheels, puffs smoke, and says 'choo! choo!' " explained White Eye. Eph had heard that the Union Pacific was building railroad tracks from the East and the Central Pacific had hundreds of Chinese coolies making a railroad from the Pacific Coast. The two companies intended to connect tracks from the Atlantic to the Pacific in northern Utah at Promontory.

"Oh, you mean the locomotive pulling many cars on iron rails?" asked Eph.

"Yes, Iron Horse smoke much, but not pipe of peace. Iron Horse scare buffalo. They run from hunting ground. Cheyenne Indians heap mad. They say, 'We kill all white man on Iron Horse.' You know Turkey Leg, big chief of Cheyennes?"

"Yes, I know Chief Turkey Leg. I've been to his lodge," replied Eph.

"You go to Turkey Leg. Tell him no shoot white man on Iron Horse—many killed. You stop bloodshed," pled White Eye.

"I can't go. My squaw says, 'You stay home with me and children.' I must remain on the ranch," said Eph. He had been looking over the wild mavericks and spotted a white-faced, white-footed, light brown animal, weighing nearly one thousand pounds. This beautiful stallion caught Eph's eye. He said, "How much you want for that cayuse?"

White Eye rapidly replied, "Heap much firewater. Me need medicine. Firewater good for red man."

"I will not give you firewater, White Eye."

"Give me gold, silver. You have heap much. Give to me for cayuse."

"No," answered Eph, "you would buy firewater with gold, silver. I give you two beef—fat. You feed family with beef." Reluctantly White Eye and Bearfoot sold the white-faced mustang to Eph for two beef cattle. With the cattle and the rest of the horses, the Indians galloped down the dusty road.

A few days of hackamore breaking followed the purchase of Whitefoot, and then Eph put the saddle on the stallion's back without much difficulty. After two days Whitefoot was accustomed to the saddle. Eph figured it was time to break the maverick for riding.

The bronc's attention was shifted to his left ear by a twist as Eph slipped into the saddle. He patted the horse's neck and rode a distance onto the range without so much as a jump from Whitefoot. Coming to a stream, the animal put his head down for a drink. After he had his fill, Eph urged him on with a gentle tickling of the spurs which roused Whitefoot into a sudden whirl of action. The fifth jump seemed as high as the moon. Coming down, the bronc twisted and reared backward and forward. With head down between his front legs he bucked furiously, which was too much for the rider who landed head first in the creek.

Two of the Hanks's hired men, observing their boss take a dive into the running water, galloped after the freed horse and succeeded in catching him. When the animal was brought back to Eph, he held firmly on the bridle and spoke to the fiery stallion, "Old Boy, that was unfair. You took advantage of me. Now I'm taking you out on the sand flat, and we'll see who is the master."

Eph mounted in regular cowboy style. As his right foot hit the stirrup, he dug both sides of the horse with his spurs and slammed his wet hat between Whitefoot's ears.

The cayuse needed no more prodding. In a flash he bounded, bucking and twisting as if he were a stick of dynamite exploding. As the white legs and the bald face fused into a ball of fire, Eph held on tenaciously until the cinch snapped, hurling man and saddle through the air. Still kicking and snorting, Whitefoot sped with enraged fury into the rock gully beyond the sand flat.

Picking himself up slowly, Eph, with a puzzled expression on his face and sand in his hair, said to his hired men, "That's enough for today. That horse has thrown me twice, fair and square. I guess I haven't much glue in my pants."

Eph sprang on the back of the horse Frank Devan was riding. Together they rode to the ranch house. They had scarcely arrived when up to the front gate rode Solomon Kimball on a lathered horse.

After a warm welcome from Eph, Solomon said, "Eph, President Brigham Young has sent me to get you to come to Salt Lake City and carry mail and important documents to Chicago. This mail is too important to be entrusted to the general mails. It must be conveyed by a trusted messenger—you, Eph Hanks."

Eph scratched his head, thought a moment, spat on the dirt, and replied, "Sol, ride posthaste to Salt Lake City and tell President Young that I'll be in his office tomorrow and will take his important mail on the Union Pacific train to Chicago."

"President Young will be pleased. I'll give him your reply." So saying, Kimball mounted his horse and began his return to Salt Lake City.

Eph walked through the kitchen door. Harriet was busy preparing dinner. "I've tacked the last board on the lean-to. Do you want to see if you approve of my carpentering?"

Harriet didn't answer his question, but asked one of her own. "What did Solomon Kimball want of you?"

"He came with a message from the Prophet. Brother Brigham has important mail and documents he wants me to carry to Chicago on the Union Pacific train."

Harriet wiped her hands on the apron tied about her waist. "Eph Hanks, if you take that mail to Chicago and leave me and the children again, I'll not be here when you return."

"But, Harriet, God's prophet has requested me to go," reasoned Eph.

"Eph, you have left me for the last time to run on errands for Brigham Young or to pacify the Indians, but no more will I concede. I have uncomplainingly stayed at home, fed the cattle, milked the cow, and done the work as I cared for the children, but no more. You either stay on the ranch with me, or I'll leave you! Do you understand?" defiantly replied Harriet.

"Harriet, I'm sorry, but when the Prophet speaks, I must obey. I'll be back, and we'll have a better life together than ever before." Eph tried to pacify Harriet but without congenial results. "You have been a good wife and mother. I am grateful for you and all you have done. I love you—stay with me that we might enjoy life together here and have an eternal family in the life to come," entreated Eph most earnestly.

"You love to leave me; that's what you do," she retorted.

Eph reached out to take Harriet in his arms, but she pushed him away, strode out of the kitchen, rushed to the bedroom, and slammed the door.

The distraught Eph Hanks, agitated with mental conflict, rode his saddle horse to Salt Lake City, received the important mail from the president of the Church, boarded the first Union Pacific train headed East, and sat on the padded seat of the passenger car oblivious to the other passengers—his thoughts on Harriet and her solemn assertion that she would leave him.

Chugging up the winding tracks in Weber Canyon,

the locomotive, pulling a long train of cars, belched steam and smoke which spilled into the open window at Eph's side. Above the explosive sound of the laboring engine, Eph overheard the conversation of the two buckskin-clad men sitting behind him.

"This railroad has thrust right into the heart of the buffalo range, and two powerful Indian nations—the Cheyennes and the Sioux—have risen up in an effort to halt the march of the empire," blurted out one of the men as he blew a whiff of smoke from his pipe.

"I heard that Red Cloud, war chief of the Sioux, sent his ultimatum," chimed in the red-bearded, round-shouldered fellow passenger. "'We no want you here. You scare away buffalo.' And Turkey Leg, head chief of Cheyennes was more threatening, more insolent."

"So I've heard," joined in the pipe smoker, "and the only answer was the shriek of the Iron Horse."

Eph recalled that White Eye had informed him of the Cheyennes' threatened attack. Would they encounter an attack somewhere en route to Fort Kearney, he wondered?

The conductor walked down the aisle and Eph stopped him. "Have you heard of any Indian attacks on the trains going east?" he inquired.

"Wild Bill Hickock with a dozen plainsmen have kept the Cheyennes pretty much in check," replied the conductor as he continued his stride down the aisle.

Eph slept fitfully on the bumpy train the first night aboard. The train was running rapidly. The next morning as Eph was washing his face, above the rattle and roar of the train, the sound of distant firing reached his ears, then the whoops of the Indians and the defiant yells of the few white men on the imperiled train ahead were heard as they swept around a ridge into the straightaway which led to a great cloud of dust and smoke a short distance beyond.

Out on the prairie lay Cheyenne braves, shot from their speeding ponies, and here and there lay a dead horse or one screaming like a human in pain. Along the track a half dozen bodies sprawled in the grotesque postures of sudden death.

Eph recognized Turkey Leg leading the attack with Porcupine close behind, both whooping shrilly and lashing their ponies. Then the whole band of warriors swept into motion, coming straight at the train. The red wave rolled at the few defenders aboard, the ground shaking under the tread of horses, the air hideous with menacing whoops.

Fifty yards from the endangered train the wave slackened and halted as the red warriors saw the other train steaming toward them. One fierce whoop rose above the tumult and the circle of red braves disintegrated as they obeyed the command of Chief Turkey Leg, swinging westward in a long column, the sun dancing on their lances. A quarter of a mile to the west they pulled up their ponies. The two chiefs rode along in front, the brilliant colors of their war finery clearly visible.

The next minute, the train Eph was riding slowed down. The conductor rushed into the car and shouted, "If you have guns, men, get them in use. The bloody Cheyennes have attacked." Eph had his six shooter in its holster. The two men in the seat behind him seized their rifles.

All occupants of the train watched the Indians retreat and gather a short distance to the west. The red-bearded frontiersman said, "We've seen a strange thing in Injun fighting just now. I never saw Injuns make a direct attack before. It's clearly against their nature. Can't figure it out."

"They're mad at the Iron Horse plowing through their lands, that's why, but what's going on over there now?" asked the other fellow.

"Powwow," said Eph to the two buckskin-clad men behind him, "Porcupine and old Turkey Leg I can make out."

"You know those Cheyenne chiefs?" asked the man who had dumped the ashes out of his pipe when he grabbed his rifle.

"Yes, I know them. I've been to their lodges," said Eph.

First Porcupine, then Turkey Leg spoke with many gestures. "Looks like they want to attack both trains," observed Eph. "I'm going out there and petition them for peace."

Eph left his pistol on the seat and walked to the door of the passenger car.

"Man, you're crazy," cried out the red-bearded man. "They'll kill you. Hey, conductor, stop that man. He's going out to where the Cheyennes are holding their powwow."

Eph said, without stopping his brisk stride, "I know Turkey Leg. He's my friend. I'll get him to stop his attack on the trains."

Every effort made by the conductor and passengers to restrain Eph failed. He bounded off the train and walked rapidly toward the Indian gathering. Drawing nearer, the thought, "Let them shoot me—I would be relieved of my inconsolable feelings over Harriet," flooded Eph's mind as he walked briskly, and then a stronger thought, "No, I must live to get the mail to Chicago!"

The Indians saw him coming. One haughty brave shouted, "Here comes paleface! Me have his scalp!" and fitted an arrow into his bow.

"No," commanded Turkey Leg. "He friendly white. He has arm raised high in peace."

As Eph reached the congregated Indians, Porcupine shouted, "He Queant! He Queant!"

Eph was not called Queant by any other Indians but the Cheyennes; and as he walked on, he remembered how he was given that name.

It was not far from where the Indians had gathered in their powwow. Some years ago he and Jim Bridger entertained the Indians in the popular game played by mountain men and Mormon scouts called "back out".

Often they engaged in hazardous adventures. Eph and Bridger shot pine cones off each other's heads with their rifles, they roped buffalo and rode them, and they wrestled; but Bridger was no match for Hanks in this combat.

A big grizzly bear made his home in a grove of small pine trees near the bottom of the canyon nearby. The Cheyennes brought Eph and Jim the news. The two challengers decided to end their "back out" contest by bringing the grizzly out of the thicket. Bridger and his dogs took the first turn. Three dogs entered the thicket; only one came out. With his tail tucked between his legs he yipped in fright. Bridger, with a day of few conquests behind him, said to Eph, "If you will go in and get him, I'll 'back out.' "

With his long hunting knife tied securely to a sapling, into the thicket went Eph. Indians, Bridger, horses, and dogs waited patiently. The silence of the dusk was whispering in the canyon. The long shadows multiplied. Moments passed—then half an hour. Eph backed out of the brush with the long, blood-splashed knife telling its own story. The Cheyennes shouted with admiration and called him "Queant," an Indian name for bear.

Eph stood, looking up into the war-painted faces of the mounted chiefs, Porcupine and Turkey Leg. They dismounted and hugged Eph warmly. The people on the two trains looked on in amazement. They couldn't believe what they saw, and Eph never told them what happened; but, less than an hour afterward, the Cheyennes—a hundred braves on their racing ponies, with the two chiefs in the lead—rode off into the canyon where years before Eph had killed the grizzly. The firemen stoked up the locomotives, and the two trains chugged laboriously up the tracks.

If there was ever a hero among men, it was Eph Hanks to the passengers and crew on those two Union Pacific trains. He had saved their lives by his advances of peace with the Cheyenne warriors. The people not only expressed to Eph their admiration and thanks, but there wasn't anything he could want that they wouldn't supply. To them Eph was the most fearless man they had ever seen. He was a strong, straight-backed man, and the passengers were delighted to be with him. Eph had done something he was proud of, and the ride to Chicago made him feel gratitude to his God for the courage given him to venture into the Indian powwow and bring about the peaceful departure of vowed killers of the palefaces.

Eph ate and talked a great deal with a railroad official who offered him a large salary and a high position on the Union Pacific Railroad. It was an enticing temptation, but Eph could not accept the offer. He was already employed by Brigham Young in the service of the Lord.

Arriving in Chicago, Eph sought out Bill Reed's hotel. He said to the clerk, "I want the best suite in this place." The clerk stared at the westerner, excused himself, and looked up the owner. In a moment Bill entered with both arms out to embrace his friend of many years past.

"You've changed a lot, Eph," said Bill, "but I'd know you even in heaven."

"Thanks," replied Eph. "I'm glad you wouldn't have recognized me in the other place." Both men laughed heartily.

To the clerk, Bill ordered, "Give this man the best we've got."

# 11

# EPH WAVES GOODBYE

Eph frequently thought of Harriet while in Chicago. "A good wife is heaven's best gift to man," he mused, "and Harriet has been my angel with graces innumerable. She has been the balm of my life. But now she has left me." Then he thought, "I never gave her a wedding ring. Perhaps if I buy her a gold wedding band she will be reminded that our marriage was for eternity and, like the wedding band, endless."

He walked out of Bill's hotel and into the narrow and winding streets. "Brother Brigham didn't lay out this town," he thought, feeling bewildered; but he walked on. He stopped at a confectionery stand and bought candy and nuts for his children. He came upon an odd-looking chair suspended from poles from a hook to weigh a person. "Only two cents to tell how much you

weigh," said the owner. Eph had never before weigh-
ed himself, so he sat in the chair. He felt as if he were
sitting in the children's swing attached to the apple tree
at his home. A hand on a dial pointed to one hundred
and ninety-two pounds. Then he watched a man winding up a toy. He held it in his hand and gave a strong
pull at the cord. Whizz. . . the toy flew up higher than
the trees, spinning like a wheel. The man called it a
shooting star. When it came down Eph bought two of
them for his boys.

Eph continued his way along a broad, graveled
walk, shaded by rows of tall elm trees. At length he
stopped at a jewelry store and, after looking at many
gold wedding bands, selected one especially for Harriet. After a pleasant walk in a beautiful park, he boarded a streetcar for Bill's hotel. Had Harriet been with him
it would have been wonderful. "But will Harriet ever
again be with me?" sadly mused Eph. The streets were
crowded with vehicles of every description, and throngs
of people pushed their way along the sidewalk. Eph
was glad he took the streetcar.

As he entered the hotel, he met Bill and a well-
dressed man by his side. "Eph, this is Mr. Richard Burton, a famous world traveler, just returned from Salt
Lake City. When I informed him you were staying at
my hotel, he wanted to meet you."

"Pleased to meet you, Mr. Hanks," said the cordial
gentleman as he extended his hand to receive from Eph
a hearty handshake. "I have heard so many stories
about you, but you are not at all as you have been
described to me."

"What sort of chap am I supposed to be?" asked Eph.

"I was told you are a villain, a Mormon desperado, but I see you as a good-looking man with a pleasant and humorous countenance."

"Thank you," said Eph. Then his friend, Bill, joined in. "Eph I've known since he was a boy. His clear, pale blue eyes have never seen any thing or any man he was afraid of and no danger he'd ever shun."

"Yes, sir, I agree," said Burton. "Judging from his cool and quiet glance, he'd shun neither friend nor foe. It's a pleasure to meet you, Mr. Hanks."

"How did you enjoy your five-day train ride from Ogden on the Union Pacific?" inquired Hanks. "Were you stopped by any Indians?"

"No, but there were rumors a plenty of the Dalton gang robbing trains returning from the East with payroll money," replied Burton.

"The Dalton gang? Who are they?" asked Eph.

"The most desperate band of robbers to infest the Indian Territory," Burton answered.

Early the next morning Eph stepped off the platform at the Chicago station and boarded the train headed west. "Swish-sh-sh," hissed the escaping steam as the train rolled away from the depot.

Crossing the Mississippi River onto the Iowa plains, the westward-bound Union Pacific chugged along. Passing over the Missouri River and into the Nebraska Territory all went well. The train stopped at North Platte; here boarded an armed force of Indian police and railroad detectives. Eph felt more secure as the train hissed on toward Scottsbluff.

Rumors floated through the passenger car Eph was riding that the Dalton gang intended to stop the train between North Platte and Scottsbluff. Eph slept well on the hardscott bench that night, and the next morning the train stopped at the station in Scottsbluff. Here the Indian police and railroad detectives were rerouted on an eastbound train, and Eph, along with other passengers, felt uneasy when the train they were on chugged out of Scottsbluff headed for Fort Laramie.

About one o'clock the train reached Independence Rock and, a short distance from there, stopped at a water station to replenish the engine with coal and water. As it was pulling out a few minutes later, two men with black masks covering their faces jumped into the engine's cab from the tender and, holding the engineer and fireman at bay with revolvers, commanded them to run the train onto a side track and stop at a given signal. When the train stopped, the robbers tied up the two men and entered the baggage car. One bandit grabbed a pay bag containing three thousand dollars as the other dashed into the passenger car wherein sat Eph and the other passengers. With a drawn revolver, one masked bandit ordered them to drop their pistols into the aisle. He then demanded the money and jewels possessed by the passengers.

Eph was forced to deliver up his money and gold wedding band. After gathering up the gold and silver from the passengers, the masked bandit, with revolver in hand, walked backward down the aisle, his eyes covering every passenger. As he backed past Eph's seat, Eph stuck out his foot and tripped him. In his fall the bandit hit his gun hand a hard blow on the arm of one of the seats which knocked the revolver from his grasp. Eph reached down and grabbed his gun from the floor and whacked the fallen bandit on the head, knocking him unconscious just as the second masked bandit carrying the pay bag entered the passenger car. With a quick pull on the trigger Eph shot the revolver out of the bandit's hand. Two male passengers pounced on him and, after a terrific struggle, pinned the robber on the floor. The two bandits were securely tied hand and foot with strong cords. The hands and feet of the engineer and fireman were untied, and soon the train with its happy crew and passengers steamed rapidly up the track to Fort Laramie where the two bandits, now without their masks, were turned over to the authorities.

When Eph got back to his ranch at Mountain Dell, Harriet and the younger children were gone. His oldest son and the hired men informed him that Harriet had left several days before. His son spoke up, "Pa, I told Mother I was staying with you. She told me to stay and added, 'When your pa returns, tell him I'm not coming back and for him not to look for me or try and persuade me to return, for I never want to see him again.' " She had moved to Salt Lake City and settled into the adobe house Eph first built. He had verbally willed that house to Harriet.

He reminisced about his past pleasant days with Harriet. He recalled with a smile that day he caught her whistlin' by the well. He remembered with pleasure their horseback rides together; yes, of that day he held her in his arms after returning from Indian fighting in Utah Valley. "Yes—she insisted I shave off my bushy beard. And, best of all, she bore me five children." Those were the days! Gone, but never forgotten! "Would I could bring them back!" Then he breathed aloud, "I loved her; wooed her; won her; but now I've lost her. Backward, turn backward, time in your flight. Bring back Harriet again to me, even tonight."

Unbeknownst to Eph, Frank Devon had walked up and overheard his last expressed wish. "Eph Hanks," said Frank, "you did the best you could with Harriet. She was a woman who, when she made up her mind to something, neither God nor angels could change her. Maybe your best wasn't good enough. Leave it there and go on."

"On to where?" asked Eph.

"Just on," continued Devon. "Ahead not back. There is no turning back. It's all in the past."

"Even if she strongly told you I was not to come for her, I'm going to do so. Tomorrow I'll ride to Salt Lake City," firmly declared Eph.

"It won't do you any good, Eph. She's stubborn—firmly fixed in her decision. Now make up your mind to forget the past and Harriet. Counsel with Brother Brigham, the Lord's prophet. He will tell you what is best," advised Frank Devon.

"I'm going to Salt Lake tomorrow, Frank," and the old twinkle came into Eph's eye, sparked with his natural humor. "I'll take her over my checkered apron, paddle her, and bring her back home with me where she belongs."

Eph saddled his best riding horse early the next

morning and rode swiftly to Salt Lake City. Harriet was cold, curt and adamant. She met Eph at the door and told him with impenetrable hardness, "I'm through with you, Eph Hanks. Go, and may I never see you again!" Without further effort to win her back, Eph sadly turned, walked down the path and through the gate. He mounted his horse and rode along the street. To add to his distress President Brigham Young was at his winter home in St. George. It would be months before Eph would have the opportunity to consult him. In March, 1872, Harriet divorced Eph.

There was a tough cattleman named Nuck who lived near Eph's ranch in Mountain Dell. He was the leader among the reckless men who lived in that vicinity. He never hesitated to tell people he had little confidence in any of the Mormons, and he didn't believe their religion. He resorted to profanity in his ridicule of anyone who believed in prayer. He directed his remarks toward Eph Hanks in particular. He scoffingly declared many times that if he got sick he would never call "Old Man Hanks." "That old hypocrite hasn't got as much power and authority with God as my old pack mule," he sneered.

Nuck was devoted to a refined little wife, and she was loyal to him. She was born to Mormon parents, but over the years on their lonely ranch she had been influenced by her husband's scorn of religion. Eph once heard her say, "Aw, religion and prayer are nothing but a matter of hypocrisy and deception."

But the day came when, in spite of the services of the only available midwife, Nuck's wife lost her newly born baby and was lying unconscious on her bed. The midwife told Nuck there was no hope for her recovery. It was on that day that Eph rode back from his sad trip to Salt Lake City and of necessity rode past Nuck's farm house. The distraught ridiculer of religion ran out and stopped him. Nuck looked up at Eph and said, "If there is anything in earth or heaven you can do to save my wife, come in." Nuck was sobbing. He was faced with a problem he couldn't solve.

As Eph walked into the house and looked upon the dying woman, Nuck cried to God—not in profanity as had been his custom, but in a humble supplication, crying over, and over, "None but God can save her now."

Eph said to the cattleman, "Will you give God the honor and glory if your wife's life is spared?" Unhesitatingly, Nuck affirmed he would. Eph took the bottle of consecrated oil from his pocket, anointed the head of the dying woman, and asked the Lord to heal her that it might be a testimony of His goodness and mercy to all. Eph then continued on his way home.

The next day Eph rode to the cattleman's house and found Nuck's wife on the way to recovery. Thereafter Nuck was never heard to poke fun at religion, profane the name of God, or scoff at Church leaders. He always gave the Lord credit for the healing of his wife. From then on, he was Eph's warm and appreciative friend.

Almost every act Eph performed was full of charity. He was a man of God and full of the Spirit of the Lord. When he contacted President Brigham Young after Harriet divorced him, the Prophet taught Eph the law of plural marriage. He, being counselled to enter this marital relationship, decided to comply. Before Eph took this important step much happened to occupy his time, his talents, and energy in Mountain Dell.

Sickness, accidents, and many other afflictions beset Eph's neighbors. Isabel Dalton, a neighbor, had returned from Salt Lake City, having been taken there by her husband to see a doctor. After days under the doctor's care, the physician was finally convinced there was no medical skill which could help her. Hearing of Isabel's plight, Eph felt impelled to call on her. When he arrived, many of her relatives were there waiting for the end. As he looked upon the sorrowful group, the impression came to Eph that she could be healed. He advised Brother Dalton to have the women wash and anoint his wife's body so that he could seal the anointing. This was done, and then Eph Hanks laid his hands upon Isabel's head and, in sealing the anointing, promised her she would be healed and live many years and should be privileged to enjoy her family and home and accomplish much good in the Church. She was immediately healed. She lived to bear two children and to serve as a ward Relief Society president.

A little crippled boy, the cords of his legs drawn backward, was blessed by Eph. He promised the boy he would walk, run, and jump like a roe. The boy was healed. A two-year-old girl of John and Olive Curfew was afflicted with sores all over her body which caused acute suffering and hindered normal growth. Eph felt inspired to bless the child. The little body was so sore Eph had to anoint her with a feather. At the sound of

"Amen" the pain and irritation ceased, and the child fell into the first refreshing sleep she had had in days. She was promised health, strength, a long and useful life, and that she would be a mother in Israel and rear sons and daughters. The promises were all fulfilled.

While driving a team with a wagon loaded with sacks of grain through Meadow Canyon, Eph met a young teamster on a wagon en route to Salina. During a friendly conversation, the boy recognized Eph as the man who had saved his father's life during the Martin Handcart rescue years before. "Father says he owed his life to the Lord and to you," the boy explained. "You thawed out his frozen limbs with ice water, remember?"

"Yes," responded Eph, "I remember."

Many were the times Eph met some of the Saints who expressed their gratitude to him for coming to their rescue years before as they trudged west with that ill-fated handcart company. Eph mused, "The distress and hardship I endured to reach these helpless stranded handcart people was little enough for me to give to help save the lives of so many Saints walking to Zion. It was not myself, but the strength given me by the Lord which brought me to them." Eph drove to the gristmill some fifteen miles from his ranch. It was customary for the ranchers to haul their grain to the mill owned and operated by Brother Sallapey and have it ground into flour. Finding the miller's youngest daughter sick with chills and fever, "summer complaint" as they called it, Eph blessed her, and she arose and praised the Lord in song and dance. She and her mother fed him well while Brother Sallapey ground the grain into snow-white flour.

The next day Eph returned to his ranch with the load of flour, placed the sacks of flour in the pantry once kept spotless and filled abundantly by Harriet. A stroke of sadness struck him and a feeling of loneliness washed over him. Ol' Black and Roan he fed with nose bags and then led them to the pasture.

Walking back to the house, Eph said loudly to himself, "Tomorrow I'll ride Ol' Sorrell to Salt Lake and get counsel and a blessing from the Lord's prophet."

Eph entered the office of his good friend, Brigham Young. When the Lord's prophet looked up at Eph standing with hat in hand in the doorway, he said, "Friend Eph, you are pale you have lost weight. Your vigor and robust vitality are much diminished. I know of Harriet's leaving you. But you have done the Lord's bidding, and He has provided for you another—a young woman who has admired you for years, ever since you rescued her, her parents and other distressed Martin Handcart Saints. More recently you found and returned her brother, Walter, long held captive by the Sioux Indians. Go marry Thisbe Reed, Eph, and God will reward you with eternal increase seldom before experienced by mortal man."

"I'll take your counsel, Brother Brigham. I shall do as you advise," replied Eph with a smile.

"And," added the Prophet, "after you have married Thisbe Reed, I'm sending you with her on a honeymoon to San Francisco on the Central Pacific Railroad. I have important documents that only you can deliver to Elder George Q. Cannon, presently publishing and editing the *Western Standard* there." Then he added with a smile, "And I promise you will not have any more skirmishes with Indians or train robbers."

As the years had flown by since the handcart rescue, Thisbe's admiration for Eph had increased, and when Eph proposed marriage to the young lady who left London with her parents for the gospel, she readily and happily accepted. Afterward, Eph repeated to her the counsel often given by the Prophet Brigham Young, "A man's duty is to love, serve, and obey God with all his might, mind, and strength, and his prayer should be, 'Lord, what have you for me to do?' A woman should love, serve, and obey her husband with all her might, mind, and strength, and a woman should receive proper care and consideration by her husband." Thisbe pleasantly assured Eph, "I will live up to that duty as you have lived up to yours."

A few evenings later, Eph, with Thisbe at his side, stood on the platform of the last passenger car of the Central Pacific Railroad train and waved goodbye to friends who had come to bid them a happy honeymoon. Thisbe's fingers twisted softly around his wrist, crumpling the white linen of his new shirt. Her eyes followed her fingers. Eph caught her chin in both his hands. Her head fell forward upon his shoulder. As they stood, his arm around her, her hand in his, the climbing moon was glorifying the night. The glistening pathway stretched straight before them. The shining pathway to the future—the pathway of eternal love. As the newlyweds stood in the full moonlight, Eph slipped the gold wedding band on Thisbe's finger.

# 12

# FATAL BILL

Farming in the Salt Lake Valley had little appeal to
Eph during his early life. He had traded other possessions for a donkey. This donkey was a handy animal.
Eph called him Old Jack. Eph, with his legs dangling
near the ground and a shovel over his shoulder, rode
Old Jack to the field to tend to his irrigating, or at other
times he'd ride the donkey on an errand. One day,
returning from irrigating, something startled Old Jack,
and he reared backward. The shovel flipped forward,
striking the burro between the ears. Old Jack plunged
vertically with back arched and feet drawn together,
sending Eph sprawling to the ground. With a shrill hee-
haw and a snort the burro dashed through the field.
Eph limped to the house, and his wife inquired "What's
the matter?"

"Oh, that rheumatism." replied Eph with a squirming movement. "Feels like it's going to rain." Eph was tired of farming, tired of the routine of planting, irrigating, cultivating, and harvesting. This mishap settled things. He left his plow, his single tree, and his shovel and rode into the mountains. He was a farmer no longer; he was now a prospector. Eph rode over to what is today Park City. He chipped a few chunks of rocks off an outcropping of a ledge. An assay showed a high content of silver and gold. Immense riches hung near Eph in his new adventure as a prospector. Eph staked out a claim he called Green Monster. Eph became the father of Park City. His prospecting became successful, and the word spread that silver was to be had for just the chipping.

The winding trail once followed by Eph to the Green Monster claim became tramped hard and wide by men with light packs on their backs or leading pack animals to the many mining claims. One morning Eph watched a lanky stranger disappear around a bend in the trail. Eph had fed the man and given him drink, but the stranger declined to answer the questions asked him. All he said was, "My name is Bill." A heavy black beard covered a square jaw. His teeth were white and set firmly. Eph recognized in him a man whom others would give elbow room to any time. Eph jokingly said to one of his hired men, "There goes Fatal Bill," and the appellation stuck because it fit him so well.

Each fall Fatal Bill trudged down from his mountain claim for winter supplies. Eph and the other miners knew he had a claim up Silver Creek, but Fatal Bill was too adroit to ever let it be discovered. Eph often joked with Bill about hitting pay dirt. Such kidding did not set well with the stranger. He disdained being joshed by anyone, especially this Mormon who appeared to be affluent.

One day during his yearly trip to town Bill offered Eph a wager, "I'll bet my life against a bobtailed cow that inside of another year I'll be riding in style while you'll be walking by the side of jackasses."

Eph's hired men cheered Bill's wit, but their boss called his hand. "It's a good thing you bet me your life, for if you stay on your claim another year you'll have nothing more to lose."

"Well, thanks. I'll show you a thing or two," growled Fatal Bill. "I'm going to strike it rich!" With a firm tug on the lash rope, he pulled the last hitch and yelled at his pack animals as he started up the trail.

"Who is that fellow?" inquired one of Eph's men.

"He remains a mystery," answered Eph. "He's talked more today than I've ever heard him talk before. Why don't you follow him to his claim and ask him?"

"Oh, no, not me. Whoever heard that a rattlesnake won't bite? Fatal Bill is no slouch with that iron he carries on his hip. Yesterday I saw him crack a jackrabbit's head off with it."

Eph smiled and then said, "While you are talking to Bill ask him how old he is. If he shaved off his black beard he wouldn't look more than thirty."

Spring arrived, and the air seemed to ring with the sound of minerals being chipped from the mountains. Eph's Green Monster proved a rich vein of ore and lined his pockets with gold. This mine led to the building of Park City. Soon the road from Salt Lake City swarmed with teams taking out ore and bringing in supplies.

Fall came with the green leaves turning to yellow and red, and with the fall colors came Fatal Bill for his winter supplies. He was disgustedly astonished to discover a new town mushrooming as if by magic. His anger was whetted when he learned that Eph's Green Monster was the cause. Since Bill's money was depleted he ventured a bold plan to obtain supplies. He concealed himself until night when darkness encompassed the area. Then he stealthily crept to Eph's supply house, broke in, and packed his horses with food and powder. Back up the trail he went, determined to strike it rich.

The theft pricked Bill's conscience, and his mind reverted to the tragedy of seven years before which had resulted in his becoming a fugitive from the law. He was again in the Bluegrass State, a young man with his lovely bride. He saw again the soft lights of the dance hall; he heard again the rhythmic music of the orchestra. Before him was the face of a young man intoxicated, forcing his attentions on Bill's bride. Bill sprang forward and roughed him up in an effort to get him outside the dance hall. The inebriated fellow reached for his six shooter, but Bill's hand was quicker on the draw, and the man crumbled on the steps. Bill fled as fast as he could to escape the consequences of his rash deed and came to Silver Creek. Bill bit his lips firmly—he was ready to file another notch on his pistol should a lawman find his whereabouts and attempt to arrest him.

After examining the horse tracks around his supply house Eph was convinced that Fatal Bill had stolen his goods and powder. He was sure the prospector had been driven to this thievery through desperation. He told his hired men, "I hope Bill finds the stolen food edible as he ekes out an existence in his lonely mountain retreat."

With the coming spring the flow of new arrivals into Park City doubled the size of the mining town. New mines were opened. With the inflow came an attractive young woman. She applied for a job at the Hanks's eating house. Before long she found favor with the male customers by her good cooking. Her smile was an invitation to the miners for their next meal. She went by the name of Jane Lowery. She soon was the sole topic of conversation among the men.

By the ore dump one noon hour as the miners were eating their lunch, one remarked, "Jane's the best lunch packer in town." The other workmen nodded their approval.

A robust chap with a deep scar across his right cheek, spoke up, "I'll give my claim in heaven just to know if she's married or not."

"Well, Long Hongry," chimed in Eph as he passed by, "I may need a few claims in heaven, so I give you my word that she is a married woman."

Another bearded miner remarked, "I'll bet she's one of the plurals."

"No," objected the man with the scar on his cheek, "She's a new arrival from the East."

"She looks to me," inserted another digger, "like

a thoroughbred from Kentucky."

The gong clanged, and the miners disappeared into the opening of the Green Monster. Long Hongry's mind was full of questions. Had she run away from her home state to hide her past? Was she following a man? Could she possibly be from his own state of Kentucky? There was something about her which seemed familiar to him. "No," he brushed aside the idea, "Her hair is not the right color for the girl I'm thinking of."

Two days later Long Hongry approached Eph. "Say, boss, as I've lost my claim in heaven to you, do you mind telling me something about Jane's husband?"

In a whisper Eph answered, "No, I can't tell you much about him. My guess is that he answers to an alias."

Long Hongry gazed at Eph bewildered, then blurted out, "I bet my last dollar he played her dirt."

"I'll take that bet," smiled Eph. "How much money have you?"

"The bookkeeper can tell you more about that, but my guess is it's close to three hundred dollars. I've worked for about five months. When you convince me Jane would be glad to meet him as a loving husband, the cash is yours."

"Now, Long Hongry, take it easy," cautioned Eph, "You've worked hard for that money. But I believe she will meet him within the next six months, and you can judge whether or not they are happy with each other."

"Fair enough," agreed Long Hongry. Walking away, he mused, "I'm glad I found out Jane has a husband. I'll leave her entirely alone. I've had enough of flirting with other men's wives." Rubbing the scar on his cheek he recalled other close scrapes he had experienced under the influence of liquor. He thought of Herman Swaggs who had shot him seven years before in a dance hall in Louisville, Kentucky, and left him for dead. He cringed when he recalled the sorrowing bride left alone when Herman fled into the unknown. Then, he well remembered, after his narrow escape from death, he had promised his mother he would never drink a drop of liquor again and that he would do all he could to bring Swagg back to his bride.

He relived his long journey west when he met the mail carrier, Eph Hanks, and how he had been influenced for good by the strength of Eph's character. Eph had given him a job on his ranch, and now he was working in the Green Monster. Well did he remember the day Eph led him into the waters of baptism and he became a member of the Mormon Church. Long Hongry was a first-class workman and a clean-living, decent man. His reformation was complete.

Things were not going well for Fatal Bill. His food supplies were diminished. The last bullet of his revolver had killed a badger, and he was eating the last of it. Luck had eluded him, and now he faced defeat. There was nothing else for Bill to do but strap on his crude snowshoes and go down the long, winding trail. As he approached the traveled road at the bend of Silver Creek, the jingle of sleigh bells, the scraping of runners, and the sound of mirthful voices reached his ears. Four white mares pranced down the snow-packed road, drawing a brightly painted sleigh.

Before Bill could elude the sleigh, its driver, and the other occupants, he looked into the eyes of Eph Hanks and his friend, Solomon Kimball. They were accompanied by their beautiful wives attired in their best winter apparel en route from Salt Lake City to the new mining town. Bill, abashed with shame, wished he could disappear in the heavy snow.

Eph called to him cordially, "Well, if it's not Fatal Bill! How did you get out of your prosperous claim this time of year?"

Humiliated beyond expression Bill would have snowshoed off a precipice were one in sight. But there was no escape. He had to face the music while Eph played the tune.

Eph stopped the snow-white mares. Kimball and the wives watched Bill. "I...I starved out," he muttered, "without striking pay dirt."

"According to our bet, then," Eph called out in mock command, "your life is mine. Pay up! Get down in that snow and roll over three times." Bill was helpless in the hands of Eph. Without a bullet, his six shooter was useless. Unstrapping the small pack from his shoulders, he turned his right hip toward Eph, who lifted the gun from its holster. Onto the snow rolled Bill. One, two, three times and up he stood. "Twice more," ordered Eph. And twice more Bill rolled in the snow.

When Bill arose, Eph was out of the sleigh and grasped Bill's hand firmly. Brushing the snow from the man's back and shoulders, Eph turned to Solomon and their wives, "I want you to meet Fatal Bill, the hermit, who broke into my commissary and stole supplies, hoping to save his life. But his life was not saved. He lost it to me on a wager. Right here in this snow we'll bury Fatal Bill forever. The man standing before us now is Herman Swaggs."

The occupants in the sleigh stared in wonderment. Swagg's body tensed with anger and contempt. His right hand dropped quickly to his hip, but the holster was empty. Eph steadied the astonished man and assisted him into the sleigh by the side of Solomon—the wives occupied the back seat. He handed him his pistol, paying no attention as to whether or not it was loaded.

"We are at your service, Herman," assured Eph. Picking up the reins, he spoke to the mares, and they were off and up the road to Park City. Eph stopped at the little barber shop and sat Herman Swaggs in the chair. To the barber he said, "I want you to give my friend the best haircut and shave you can offer. Charge it to me. I'll return in an hour."

Bill's face was pale—the ruddiness was gone. He felt uncertain. Less than an hour before he had heard his own name for the first time in seven years. No questions about himself or his past had been asked, and Bill's resentment and fear faded away. He warmed up to the barber as he lavished on him his finest lotions, soaps, and oils. Why not? The "big boss" was paying the bill.

Eph returned within the hour, paid the barber and escorted Herman—no longer Bill—to the commissary. Here he was outfitted into new clothes. Eph looked at the now handsome young man and said, "I would have never recognized you as once being Fatal Bill."

Eph, with Herman by his side, walked over to the lodge. Here they found Long Hongry bent over a sheet of paper, writing to his mother. Looking up from his writing, Long Hongry arose and inquired, "Mr. Hanks, I'm glad to see you, but who is he?"

Eph replied, "Frank Devan, this is Herman Swaggs, the man who left you for dead seven years ago."

Both men stood mute, dazed, until Frank grasped Herman's hand. Herman swayed, almost too overcome to stand on his feet. He was visibly trembling, markedly relieved, and grateful to know that he was not a murderer. With quivering lips and eyes misty with tears, he breathed, "God knows I'm glad you are alive."

"I'll call for you in ten minutes, Herman," called Eph over his shoulder as he left the two young men alone. After a short absence he stood in the doorway and said, "Come now, Swaggs. We'll let Frank Devan finish his letter."

Moments later the two men walked into the eating house where Herman held his astounded and beloved Jane in his arms in a warm embrace.

Turning on his heel, Eph spoke over his shoulder as he left the dining room. "Mrs. Swaggs, give Herman plenty to eat, and we'll put him on the payroll immediately."

# 13

---

# THE TRADING POST

After the Utah War, Eph moved to a secluded valley between Big and Little Mountains east of Salt Lake City. He called his newly acquired ranch Mountain Dell. Here he built a trading post and developed a thriving business; hundreds of immigrants passed by on the way to the Great Salt Lake valley. He provided a plate of hot refreshments for the travelers before they sped on their way eastward or westward.

During the winter months, snow fell heavily in the Mountain Dell valley. Eph had great difficulty keeping the road open over Big Mountain. The snow near the east brink often drifted to depths of ten and twelve feet. To open the road for winter travelers, Eph used his sturdy yoke of oxen, Buck and Blow. He drove them into the drifted bank as far as he possibly could, then he unyoked them. Buck knew what being unyoked meant—he plunged forward until he penetrated into the snow up to his eyes. The big ox tramped around until he made a solid footing preparatory for his next move. Then that old bovine bunted into the snow bank with such robust energy that Eph feared he would lose him forever in the deep drift, but the sturdy beast always backed out of the drift. Then old Buck snorted and bucked, and the drifted snow bank crumbled under his powerful bunting.

The Wells Fargo stagecoach stopped at Eph's trading post. Eph stood in admiration of the Concord coach, hand-crafted to meet the challenge of the mountain roads, the rock-strewn trails, and long downgrades demanding strong brakes. The Concord coach hugged the road because of its low center of gravity and springy, slung-through braces. Four to six splendidly matched horses swiftly drew the gaily painted coach with its polished trappings. The Concord could carry nine passengers inside and several more outside. These included the driver and the shotgun rider—keen-eyed protector of the treasure box beneath the seat. This famous green Wells Fargo box that brought danger and daring into the dashing drives over the western roads might be filled with thousands of dollars in gold dust or bullion, and the roaming highwaymen knew it. This wild, reckless breed of highwaymen attempted 347 robberies during the fourteen years the stage stopped at Eph's way station.

One day Eph walked out to greet the driver and

his passengers. They all piled out, pale, subdued, and so solemn they spoke not a word as they moved slowly into the trading post. When Eph inquired of "Sandy Dan," the famous stagecoach driver, what had happened, he took off his dusty hat, spat in the dirt, and said, "About ten miles back we were held up by a masked bandit who demanded we throw the green box down to him. But I gave up hard. I expressed my doubt that one man was capable of such a rash feat. The careless bandit boasted that he was quite alone. So I exclaimed, 'Well, who are they behind you, then?' It was a fatal instant for the bad man as he glanced around. The heavy end of my lash fell, crashing on his head. When he came to he found himself bound hand and foot. Up the road aways we turned him over to your deputy marshall, Port Rockwell."

"Say now," said Eph, "I'm sure after such an experience you and the passengers are not only shaken, but hungry. So, Sandy Dan, come join the others for a special feast I have prepared."

Eph knew that the passengers who crossed the plains and traveled over the mountains were generally rich or they couldn't afford the ride, so those who stopped at his station were people who were able to pay their way, and Eph aimed to give each passenger his money's worth.

At the time Eph was expecting this Wells Fargo stagecoach with its load of passengers, beef was scarce. But, determined to keep his table supplied with fresh meat, he had gone out and killed several badgers and hedgehogs. For two days he boiled the meat in several changes of water. The strong wild taste and smell were gone. When he served this meat to the high-toned strangers, they smacked their lips and asked for more. One of the diners was a rich banker going with his wife to California. He enjoyed several slices of boiled badger and asked, "Mr. Hanks, what kind of meat have you served us? I have never tasted anything quite so good."

With a twinkle in his eye Eph answered, "Mr. Banker, that is cub, our common Mountain Dell cub."

The banker, turning to his wife, said, "Yes, I thought so. It is certainly the most delicious meat that has been set before us since we left home."

Neither telegraph line nor railroad track yet crossed the wastes of prairie, mountain, and desert between the Missouri River and Sacramento, California. By 1860 there were half a million goldseekers, homesteaders and others west of the Rockies. These pioneers had sought the aid of Congress for a faster overland mail service. And so on April 3, 1860, the Pony Express, the West's own enterprise, began carrying the nation's news across the continent faster than it had ever been carried before. The news of the new service stirred the imagination— "Mail for Utah, California, Oregon, Washington Territory, British Columbia, the Pacific Mexican Ports, the Russian Possessions, the Sandwich Islands, China, Japan, and India."

Eph was excited with the prospects and wanted to be a participator—yes, a Pony Express rider—but when he applied, he sadly learned that he was too heavy and too old. Disappointed in not being eligible as a mail carrier, he set up a Pony Express Station at Mountain

Dell. So, night and day, from horse to horse, from rider to rider, from station to station, the mail went through, and somewhere beyond Salt Lake City the eastbound riders saw the westbound, looming out of the sunrise. They passed at a gallop with a wave of the hand—two flying shuttles on the loom of the continent, weaving the fabric of the Union. And Eph stayed up most of the night to supply both riders a fresh mount and a tasty morsel of food before the riders continued to the next post.

The westbound mail made the trip in nine days and twenty-three hours. This new mail service was organized by Russell, Majors, and Waddell, a well-known express firm of Leavenworth, Kansas. The firm had set up 190 relay stations, and although Eph's was only one, it *was* one, and he was involved. He was one of the four hundred employees, and he cared for six of the four hundred and eighty horses worth $200.00 each. The eighty riders were the pick of the West. Two of Eph's Mormon friends were among them, Howard Eagan and Sam Wilson. These riders rode for salaries of $50.00 to $150.00 a month, depending on the length and dangers of the run. But they rode especially for the love of adventure. Most of the riders were small— jockey size—and in their early twenties. Each was required to take an oath: "I will not use profane language, will drink no intoxicating liquors, and will not quarrel or fight with any other employee." The firm presented each man with a Bible when he took his job and expected him to uphold high standards, even in the rough-mannered, tough-living towns of the West.

Postal rates by Pony Express were expensive: $5.00

for each half ounce, later reduced to $1.00. Letters were written on onionskin paper, and newspapers sent condensed versions on thin stock. The British government used the service for important Asiatic mail. News in this country was never more vital than at that moment, for the Union was reaching a crisis. The Pony Express bore westward the news of Lincoln's election, the firing on Fort Sumter, and the president's call to arms.

Among the applicants for this most dashing and dangerous job—the dream of all boys of the period—was a slim lad by the name of William Cody who said, "The fellers call me Bill." The manager looked him over and hesitated, because the run in his division was one of the most dangerous; but the manager never knew that this boy would go down in fame as Buffalo Bill.

The day Cody stopped at Eph's station for a fresh mount and refreshment, he had escaped from fifteen armed Sioux Indians by sheer horsemanship, outriding them on his swift pony for twenty-four miles. A few months later he proudly told Eph, "I have broken all records for endurance in a run of 322 miles without a stopover."

There rode into Eph's post one evening "Pony Bob" Haslem, his horse lathered with sweat and foam. His relief rider had failed to show up, and he had ridden 185 miles through Ute-infested desert. When he got to the next station he found the place in smoldering embers, the body of the station master mutilated, and all the stock stolen. On he rode to Eph's station, where Eph insisted he snatch some sleep, eat a substantial meal, and wait the arrival of his relief rider.

When Eph learned that marauding bands of Indians had overrun the roadway leading into the Salt Lake Valley he left Mountain Dell to the care of Thisbe and the older boys, and spent much of his time among the hostile Indians of the plain. He visited one tribe after another. By his wise and understanding diplomacy he saved the lives of many people. All this service he gave without remuneration—for his love of God's children, both white and copper-skinned, knew no bounds.

Eph observed much good in his friendly and fearless encounters with the Indians. In the dusky interior of a smoky tepee, an Indian woman bent over the new baby on her lap. At the noise of his entry, the tiny, red-brown face puckered up. The mother caught the little nose gently between her thumb and forefinger and with her palm over the mouth stopped the cry soundlessly. When the baby began to twist for breath, she let go a little. At the first sign of another cry she shut the air off again, softly crooning a Cheyenne growing song to make the son straight-limbed and strong of body and heart. An old Indian grandmother told Eph that Indian mothers always shut off the first cry of the newborn and as often after as necessary. This is to teach the most important lesson of old Indian life: no one can be permitted to endanger the people, no cry must guide a skulking enemy to the village or spoil a hunt that might mean the winter's meat for the tribe. Eph learned that this new baby's life would never be touched by a punishing hand. He would be made equal to the demands of his expanding world without physical chastisement. Eph noted with profitable interest that the Indians he spent time with avoided any overprotection of the young, particularly a mother's favoritism for the eldest son.

When an Indian boy began to crawl no one would cry, "No, no!" and drag him back from the enticing red of the fire. To Eph, the Chief said, "One must learn from the bite of the flame to let it alone." The boy swam well before he could walk, and so it was safe to let him play around the placid river.

The young Indian's attitude toward girls was established early. Eph heard an old Cheyenne saying: "See how the boy is with the women of his lodge and you can know how the young man will be with your daughter." Over-familiarity was discouraged when seven or more lived about a winter fire. The father had the place of honor at the back, the youths and boys to his left, the women and girls to the right, with an old woman as keeper of the entrance, noting all who came and went. Such close living demanded a well-established pattern of conduct if there was to be order and peace during the confining winter months.

Eph learned from the Sioux that the sky, the earth, and the four winds together are the great powers in whom man and nature are united in brotherhood. In such a philosophy, hatred can never be harbored, not even hatred for an enemy. During the inter-tribal conflicts of the buffalo days, war prisoners sometimes became wives of chiefs and returned to visit their people with their husbands. Captured men and boys, too, might be taken into the tribe. Eph learned that Sitting Bull's adopted brother was a war captive and was honored all his life by the Sioux. Only when a renegade got control of some young warriors were the Indians dangerous to whites, as Eph was soon to learn when the Black Hawk War broke out.

Leaving one tribal village, Eph came upon on old man dancing gravely by himself on a little knoll. With sign talk and pictures drawn in the dust, he told Eph the story of the old woman who lived in the moon, which was just rising full out of the east. The old man pointed to the burden of wood he had hurriedly gathered before the storm that always followed the moon's first waning. He had come to this spot to dance because fifty snows ago a great chief of his tribe had been left on a burial scaffold to return to the grass that fed the buffalo, who would in turn feed the Indian.

Eph learned that the Sioux and Cheyenne had no fear of death and no uneasiness about the dead. Children saw sickness, the dying, the burial, and often went alone to visit the burial place.

Eph met with a gathering of Indians thirty miles east of the Green River on Big Sandy in his efforts to keep the peace, not only with the whites, but also among several tribes. There were one hundred lodges. Many of the Indians were old acquaintances of Eph: To-Sharpooe, or White Eye, To-Ko-Woonah and his father, Sowiette. They received Eph kindly. Eph reminded them of their obligation in keeping off the territory of the Sioux, Shoshone, Arapahoes, Cheyennes, and Crows. The Indians thought it hard to give up their annual buffalo hunt on the Platte River and tributaries but promised to keep off other tribes' lands except by consent of the tribes who possessed that territory.

The Indians loved and respected Eph, and he wielded an influence among them that was little short of marvelous. Eph's popularity with the Indians was due mainly to his kind treatment of them. Furthermore, Eph was willing to learn from the Indians, and they knew from experience that he had a special influence with the Great Spirit.

Business at Mountain Dell dropped off abruptly after a new road through Parley's Canyon was completed, and Eph considered moving where the traffic was to be found. One day in April, 1865, before he made his move, he felt apprehensive regarding some event which would have a detrimental effect upon the Mormon community. He couldn't account for this anxiety. He was prompted to watch from the hilltop above his station, fearing he should be on the alert. He settled himself against the gnarled trunk of an ancient spruce and slowly surveyed the road, once heavily traveled by immigrants, stagecoaches, and Pony Express riders. The sky was clear, the air crisp, and the scent of mountain flowers poignant. Eph studied the ridges, swinging his gaze southward. The hills were green and empty. His goats and sheep were grazing, and his son, Walter, was herding them. All was quiet except for the singing mountain birds in the trees above him. Suddenly, far to the southeast, his eyes caught glimpses of three riders speeding down the winding roadway. He kept his eyes on them. Within moments he recognized the riders as Ute Indians on pinto cayuses. To stop them and learn of their destination, Eph scampered down the rugged hillside to the road below. He had scarcely reached the seldom-traveled roadway when the three Indians rode up and stopped.

Pan-now-nup, an Indian well-known by Eph, and a peaceful sort of redskin, raised his hand and greeted, "How, Eph! Me come fast like rabbit from Diamond Fork—band of bad Indians ride down Maple Canyon, kill two palefaces, steal cows, and ride away. In Thistle Valley more bad Indians, kill white man, squaw, four papooses, run off much horses and cows. Bad!"

Eph inquired, "Who's heading these attacks, Pan-now-up?"

Wanzitz, on another lathered, heavy-breathing pony said, "Black Hawk, him bad. We good Indians, no want war with Mormon friends. Come, Eph, come make peace with Black Hawk. He listen to you."

To Eph it sounded as though the Indians had resorted to their old tactics, used during the Walker War years ago, of separating in all directions and attacking small groups of Mormons and slaughtering indiscriminately. He inquired, "Can't Chief Arapeen halt these attacks and control Black Hawk?"

"Arapeen die, go to happy hunting ground. He die with good feelings for all palefaces. But Jake, his son, rode into Manti for big talk—bad temper, boast he kill fifteen Mormon cows, he kill more. Paleface Lowery full of firewater, pull Jake by hair off pony—go for gun. Jake mad, jump on pony, ride to Black Hawk. Come help, Eph—no want fight."

But the third Indian, Pie-ka, said, "Eph, take your squaw and papooses to Chief Brigham in city—Black

Hawk come here, kill them, run off sheep, cows—then you come to us."

Eph understood the precarious situation which was created by the wily Black Hawk who, with a number of other subchiefs, had not attended a treaty and peace gathering held by the superintendent of Indian affairs with President Young and several Church leaders. Eph, his face wrinkled and grave, his hands clasped together—expressive of his deep concern—spoke in a voice as of resonant brass as he waved in gesture to the three, poorly clad Indians, "I'll do as you suggest, my redskin friends. Thank you for the warning. I'll see you soon."

Within a few days Eph moved his family and stock into the Salt Lake Valley and met with President Young in the hope of receiving his sanction for the peace mission he was soon to undertake. But President Young said firmly, "Eph, I will not give you my blessing. I do not want you to go. Black Hawk would not listen to me, although he knows I do not speak with a forked tongue, and he will not listen to you. He'll put an arrow through you. You stay in the valley. Black Hawk will come to you. Mark my word."

Surprised and disappointed, Eph listened but uttered no protest. Then continued the Prophet, "After this Black Hawk conflict is over, I'm sending you to the Colorado to start a settlement, build a ferry, and direct the crossing of Saints who will be called to settle Arizona."

This was an unexpected setback, but Eph shouldered his disappointment and spent the next months with Thisbe and his children in the great Salt Lake Valley.

Dozens of Mormon men who engaged in the Black Hawk War, claimed the honor of killing Black Hawk. In reality this Indian chief who was responsible for the many raids on Mormon communities was wounded severely in the fight at Gravelly Ford on the Sevier River, but he lived three years after the wound. Before Black Hawk's death, he obtained permission from the military authorities of the Utah Territory to visit all the villages and ranch areas where he and his tribe had raided. He then encountered Eph and implored him to accompany him as he went to each place and begged the pardon of his Mormon friends he had so sorely injured. He rode with Eph and seven of his warriors into every town from Cedar City in the south to Payson on the north and made peace with the people.

Eph, acting as interpreter, told the Mormons for the renegade chief, Black Hawk, that he was returning to his home to die after he made peace with his much-injured friends. "Me go to happy hunting ground," he said. Black Hawk died in his wigwam near Spring Lake in 1870 and was buried in the foothills. He had come to Eph as the Prophet had predicted.

# 14

# EPH ENTERTAINS TWO U.S. MARSHALS

Early one wintry morning, Eph left his ranch on horseback for Salt Lake City. He attended to business matters and called on his good friend, Brigham Young, who advised, "Eph, I want you to sell your ranch and move to Lee's Ferry on the Colorado River and settle there. You can help the immigrants cross that big river and direct their settlement in Arizona."

Eph thought a moment and replied, "As the Lord's prophet speaks, His servant will comply."

Late in the evening Eph started for the ranch. Clouds hung low; a foot of snow covered the ground. Entering the canyon which led to the ranch, Eph rode into a severe blizzard and intensely strong freezing wind filled with snow which made riding a horse almost impossible. Difficult though it was to get through the snowdrifts with the road completely obliterated, Eph urged his weary horse on as the blizzard violently intensified. Knowing it was his only chance, he gave the horse free rein. The animal instinctively took Eph to his ranchhouse.

Past midnight, Eph put the faithful horse into the barn, fed him, and then stumbled his way to the ranch house. Thisbe had the lantern burning in the window. With extreme difficulty, Eph pulled off his boots. His feet were badly frozen. Thisbe arose and brought her husband a tub of ice water. By placing his frozen feet into the icy liquid, Eph drew the frost from his feet, but the toes on his left foot were frozen to the bone. He had them amputated in a day or two when a doctor arrived. Eph directed the amputation and refused to take the anesthetic the doctor wanted to administer. Thisbe and others in the room could not endure the sight of the surgery and departed to another part of the house.

The year following this incident, President Brigham Young died. The prophet's passing was a sorrowful shock to Eph, and he was determined to sell the ranch and travel with Thisbe and their children to Lee's Ferry, but, upon the advice of President John Taylor, he moved instead to a location in eastern Wayne County. He selected a secluded spot in a box canyon. The site was beautiful, even inspiring, with gigantic crags and walls of solid rock. In the center of this isolated, elongated depression between the walls of stone, flowed a lovely, clear, sparkling stream called Pleasant Creek, which emptied into the Fremont River further down the canyon. The soil was rich and productive, the climate warm and adapted for raising fruit, gardening, and growing sugar cane, corn, and grain. This acquired land was the most fertile and picturesque in the entire area.

Eph and his boys built a comfortable home and corrals and sheds for horses, sheep, and cattle. He planted crops and set out two hundred fruit trees. These were happy years for Eph, although lean ones, for money was scarce. Eph, Thisbe, and children worked early and late, improving and beautifying the new home which they named Floral Ranch. The pleasant-to-the-eye frame house was erected on a bench far enough back for flower beds and lawn grass in front. Bathed in the summer sunshine, the well-planted gardens, grain fields, and orchards, blended with the grace and dignity of the massive cliffs which provided strength and protection to Floral Ranch.

People were always welcome at the ranch. The Hanks's cordial reception of guests won for their home the appellation of "Hanks Hospitable Ranch."

Nine years after settling Pleasant Creek Valley, Eph's son, Walter, received a mission call to Chicago. Though Eph lacked money to send him, he was determined his son should fill that mission. Walter had but a month to get ready for his mission. He helped his father put in the crops, made a trip to Teasdale with molasses, dried fruit, and corn, and brought back flour and other needed supplies. All available means had been spent to improve the farm and the home.

Thisbe and Walter were worried, but Eph seemed cheerful and optimistic that the way would be provided and money would be forthcoming. If the money failed he would take a pack horse to carry bedding and provisions and go with Walter to Chicago on horseback. Eph had made that trip many times, and he was sure it would not hurt Walter to take the trip once on horseback. The Lord had never failed Eph yet, and he did not expect Him to do so now.

Walter and his fiancee, Mary Stewart, decided to get married before he went on his mission. Mary's mother, Ellen, living in Teasdale, sold two four-year-old steers for forty dollars and gave the money to them for a wedding present. This provided Walter money for his transportation to Chicago. At his farewell dance, Walter received enough money in contributions from friends and relatives, to buy a suit of clothes, books, and other necessities. In fact, he had twenty-five cents left in his pocket when he arrived in Chicago. Mary supported her husband on his mission by teaching school while he was gone.

Eph and Thisbe received word that their friends, Bill Arnold and his wife, were moving from Salt Lake City into Wayne County. Eph drove to Salina, the nearest railroad town, to bring the Arnolds the seventy-five miles to Floral Ranch. With the Arnolds, their young children, and belongings, Eph began his return to the ranch. While his teams were pulling the heavy load up King Meadows Canyon, a heavily loaded outfit going down to Salina stopped, and the driver waved to them.

Eph said, "Whoa," to his team and saluted the

young man on the heavily loaded wagon. Learning that Eph was from Wayne County, the young man inquired, "Do you know a man named Eph Hanks?"

"I guess you have met the fellow right here," came Eph's reply. "What's on your mind, young man?"

The young man stepped down from the wagon, walked over to where Eph sat, and gripped his hand with a firm shake. "My father told me if I ever met you, I was to bring you down to Cedar City. Let him lay eyes on you, and you will not get away in a hurry—"

"Sounds good," agreed Eph, "but who is your father?" The young man told him. "Well, well," broke in Hanks heartily, "I am sure glad to hear from your father. He was in the Martin Handcart Company of fifty-six, snowed in on the Sweetwater."

"Yes. Father has told me how he was frozen and laid out for dead, but you administered to him, and he revived. You thawed out his frozen limbs with ice water."

"Yes, he was far gone," Eph nodded.

"Father says he owes his life to the Lord, and to you a debt of gratitude he can never repay. Father is healthy now. He owns a big ranch and a herd of high-bred cattle. The Lord has blessed him with a family. I am his oldest son."

"Yes, you look like him."

"Our home is not more than thirty miles from here." The young man looked eagerly into Eph's face. "Will you go with me now?"

Eph shook his head. "No. We must get this young family to Floral Ranch. But tell your father I have not forgotten him and that I will come to your home as soon as I can, which will not be over a year."

The young man shook Eph's hand warmly and went on his way.

The next fall after the work was done, Hanks saddled Old Dick. To Thisbe he said, "I'm going to see a friend. Don't worry about me."

After three weeks' absence his return was made in elegant style. He drove up to Floral Ranch in a new wagon, drawn by a prancing team of horses. His saddle horse, Old Dick, was tied behind the wagon. He brought home a wagon filled with sacks of potatoes, a sackful of peach pits for planting, and many packages of seeds. Also in the wagon was a molasses mill made from government steel tires, burned off the supply wagons destroyed by fire along the Big Sandy. By the mill were blacksmith tools, farm implements, a set of harnesses, and horse shoes enough to supply Floral Ranch for years.

"Well," exclaimed Thisbe, "that man was one man who remembered!" And as Eph swept her into his embrace, she knew, too, for she was one of them. What deep gratitude filled the hearts of the members of the handcart company whenever they thought of him— the man with resourcefulness, endurance, and courage enough to rescue them.

Eph and Thisbe were consistent in teaching their children gospel principles and were punctual in having them baptized. Their children had good examples to follow in their parents and were faithful to the covenants they made with the Lord. However, Eph and Thisbe said little to their children either for or against plural marriage, although the children knew their father had two other wives besides their mother and that there were children belonging to these wives.

Shortly before President Wilford Woodruff issued the Manifesto declaring that the Church would obey the Edmund-Tucker Law which had made plural marriage a criminal offense, most of the brethren practicing polygamy were either in the territorial penitentiary or had been incarcerated elsewhere from one to three years and forced to pay fines from one to three hundred dollars. After the Manifesto, the men were allowed to support their wives and children but not to live with more than one wife. Yet there were children born to some polygamist wives which evidenced the breaking of the law. These were dubbed "cohabs," or those who practiced "unlawful cohabitation." Many of the men and their wives entangled with this law fled with their families to Old Mexico. For the United States marshals in Utah territory, to round up "cohabs" was a lucrative business. For every conviction of an unlawful cohabitation each marshal received a fee of fifty dollars.

One day two deputy marshals in a light, open-topped buggy drawn by a rangy team of horses, drove to Floral Ranch. As it turned in across the bottom lands, a man in a bent-over posture working part way up the steep slopes near the bench above Eph's ranch house observed their approach. At the sight of the buggy and team, he stepped quickly behind a pile of rocks and, raising his right arm high, waved it in three wide sweeps toward the south. Eph's half-grown son, Sidney, caught the man's signal. Off he ran in the direction of the Wright's ranch up the canyon, stopping only to close and carefully fasten two gates.

As the deputy marshals turned their team and buggy to cross the bottom lands, a wagon which had been parked on the slope of the bench with one back wheel blocked suddenly rolled back against the corral fence crossways on the road.

"Hey!" said Pete to the other marshal, "did you see anyone pull that block out?"

"What block?" demanded Mack.

"The wagon over there." Pete nodded his head toward the wagon.

"Say! Doggone!" Mack sat up straight. "A minute ago it was up above the road—and now it's across. We can't get by."

Pete jerked out the whip. "Just what I was a tellin' ya. We'll have to drive across Hanks's lawn. And Wright—"

"Wright'll have time to make his getaway. Damn it!" exclaimed Mack disgustedly.

When they arrived at Eph's door, he invited the two deputy marshals to supper. After a filling meal and a thank you to Thisbe, the three men walked out on the porch.

"Take this Congress chair, Pete," invited Eph. "Guess you fellows are a little tired."

Behind the kitchen door, Eph's son, Sidney stood up against the wall listening. He had heard that anyone shielding a "cohab" was sentenced to one year in the penitentiary and subjected to a heavy fine. He didn't like the looks of the two deputies. His heart thumped when he realized how close he was standing to these dangerous men.

"Mack and I," Eph continued, "will each take a sack of husks and sit on the bench."

The marshals took out their sacks of Bull Durham, filled their pipes, and were soon enveloped in a cloud of tobacco smoke.

Something mysterious had shut out the turmoil of the day from the two visitors on the porch. Could it have been the enchantment of the fragrant peach orchard bathed in the moonlight, or was it the twitter of the night birds calling in the dark, or possibly the faint sound of the running water of Pleasant Creek gliding through Floral Valley? The glorious sight of the full moon rising over the towering two-thousand foot cliff was breathtaking. And then from the kitchen came the sweet young voices of the girls as they washed the supper dishes, singing their Sunday School hymn, "We are the bees of Deseret."

For the moment they forgot the fifty-dollar reward that had escaped them that afternoon; forgot even that the news of their presence was being carried hastily from ranch to ranch, warning the "cohabs" to flee from the wrath suddenly come upon them.

Breathing deeply the fresh spring air, Mack remarked, "Eph, you have a lovely ranch here in this most peaceful, beautiful valley."

"Yeah," said pessimistic Pete. After a long puff of smoke escaped between his lips he muttered, "If his little haven was rid of those damn law-breakin' neighbors."

"I'm afraid," Eph inserted promptly, "you haven't the respect for our neighbor, Mr. Wright, that I and my family have learned to have."

"No," Pete snapped, "we haven't. I suspected you didn't want to see him caught when we found that wagon blocking the road."

"Wagon?" Eph inquired innocently.

"Yeah," Pete went on. "The wagon across the road that forced us to turn up to your house, across your lawn, and over your wife's rose garden. And then your pressing invitation to stop with you while our horses rested here delayed us."

"Hold on a minute," broke in Mack. "Don't accuse our host of aiding and abetting Wright's getaway."

Inside the kitchen door, the boy's fingers gripped the door frame and his ruddy cheeks paled.

"Oh, no," said Pete, as he drew a whiff from his pipe and laughed quickly. "If it wasn't for our friend, Eph, we might be sleeping tonight out under some cottonwood tree with no food for ourselves or horses."

Mack cradled his pipe in his hand. "You can't trace anything to Eph."

"Sure not," added Pete, pausing. "But them two gates we had to stop and open—no doubt they've always been kept shut." With a faint sneer in his voice, Pete added, "And that pair of cowboy boots laying at the side of the road as we went up to Wright's house—well, of course they didn't show the owner could run faster without 'em on his feet!"

Mack laughed, "When we came back those boots got tired of waiting and had got up and walked off."

"Yeah!" Pete flashed a bitter look at Eph. "I wonder—"

The boy inside the kitchen door winced, and his hair stuck up a little higher on his head as he glanced down at his own footwear and wondered if this man was a detective like the ones he had read about in books and the newspaper. Sidney muttered to himself, "Standing behind that pile of rocks, Johnny Giles gave me three waves of his arm, and I guess there was nothing wrong with me running half a mile and slamming two gates and giving the three waves to Wright; sure there was nothing wrong with that." He knew Wright had ducked into the sagebrush quickly on the signal and had made for the creek under cover of the sage. Once he was in the water, the marshals could not tell which way he had gone.

Out on the porch, Mack said, "Well, we ain't paid for secret service work; we get our pay for bringing cohabs to court. Supposin' we let this matter drop?"

"Yes," agreed Eph, "I'll call out the girls, and they'll sing us a song."

He called to the boy behind the door, "Sidney, you and Ray push the organ close to the frontroom door. Nettie, bring out my triangle, and, Lillie, give us a chord on the organ."

Soon Eph, Thisbe, and children sang:

School thy feelings, O my brother.
Train thy warm impulsive soul.

Do not let emotions smother,
But let wisdom's voice control.

School thy feelings, condemnation
Never pass on friend or foe,
Though the tide of accusation
Like a flood of truth may flow.
Hear defense before deciding
And a ray of light may gleam,
Showing thee what filth is hiding
Underneath a shallow stream.

Lillie pulled an old tattered songbook from under the organ bench, and the family sang "Old Black Joe," "My Old Kentucky Home," and "O Susannah." The deputy marshals joined in with a good tenor and bass.

"You boys," invited Eph, "put on your dancing shoes and come out on the porch and give us a hornpipe."

"Yes, do one of those ol' jig dances," chorused Pete and Mack.

The boys readily responded, especially Sidney who welcomed the chance to change his shoes. Ray and Sidney danced some fancy jig steps to the chords played on the organ and to the time beaten by their father on the triangle. Afterward they received a loud applause from the deputies.

"My wife and son," said Mack, "go to your Sunday School in Salt Lake, and they often hum some of the tunes of songs you sing. Could you sing, 'We Thank Thee, O God, for a Prophet?' "

As the family finished, Pete spoke up rather suddenly, "Can you sing the song about tea and coffee?"

"We sure can," chimed in the children, and with father and mother joining with them they sang:

> In our lovely Deseret,
> Where the Saints of God have met,
> There's a multitude of children all around.
> They are generous and brave,
> They have precious souls to save,
> They must listen and obey the gospel sound.
> That the children may live long,
> And be beautiful and strong,
> Tea and coffee and tobacco they despise,
> Drink no liquor, and they eat
> But a very little meat.
> They are seeking to be great
>      and good and wise.
>
> Hark, hark, hark! 'Tis children's music,
> Children's voices, Oh, how sweet.
> When in innocence and love,
> Like the angels up above,
> They with happy hearts
>      and cheerful faces meet.

Sidney noticed that when the word "tobacco" was mentioned in the song the two marshals took their pipes and knocked the tobacco from the bowls onto the ground in front of the porch.

"Now," said father Eph, when the concluding notes

of the song ended softly, "some of you young children should go to bed, so we'll have evening prayers."

Ray and Sidney ran and moved the front room chairs in a circle, and all members of the family knelt as usual in prayer. Mack knelt with them, but Pete sat on a chair with bowed head.

Eph prayed. He asked God to bless the prophet and authorities of the Church. He implored the Lord to bless his family. Then for a very special occasion, he prayed, "We thank thee for such officers of the law as we entertain this evening who are not bent on persecution of some of the scattered brethren, but only on enforcement of the laws of the land! We are grateful for the Manifesto given to thy prophet, and for the disposition of the majority of the Saints to live up to the same. We thank Thee that these officers with us tonight are unlike some who frighten people by forcing themselves into these sacred homes with a pistol in one hand and a search warrant in the other. Preserve these friends from accident and harm that they may return home in safety."

As they arose from their knees, Thisbe said, "When these gentlemen are ready for bed, Father, you can show them into the boys' bedroom." She then turned to Ray and Sidney. "Boys, move back the organ, and I'll make your bed here on the floor of the front room."

Eph and his guests returned to the porch while Sidney, the boy who had closed two gates and passed on three waves to neighbor Wright, lay sleepless on the quilts which his mother had placed on the floor. For an hour he listened to his father and the men, chatting to one another on the porch.

"Eph," started out Mack, "you've got three families, but you haven't got three wives now. Tell us how you fixed this all up."

Eph explained slowly, "You fellows know us Mormons well enough to realize what a blow this Edmund-Tucker law against plural marriage was. Look at me for instance. Some years ago I married Harriet Little, a young widow. I would raise children to Little; they would be his in eternity, as the Bible says: '...Moses said, if a man die, having no children, his brother shall marry his wife, and raise up seed unto his brother.' " Mack nodded his head.

Eph continued, "Harriet divorced me and I later married Thisbe Reed, who was one of the members of the handcart company coming over the mountains. Then under the law of our Church, I later on married a young girl, Jane Capener. Jane and Thisbe's children will be mine through all eternity as they will be my wives worlds without end. Thisbe fully understood this and gave her blessing to this union.

The cry of the nightbird wavered through the stillness. Sidney, wide awake on his bed on the floor, thought what a busy man his father must have been in those days, carrying the mail and fighting Indians while he had three families to care for.

"But," interrupted Pete, "you haven't got two wives now." Then, straightening in the Congress chair queried, "Or have you?"

"No," Eph replied, "but all three of the women I've married have got some mighty fine sons." He mentioned by name the sons of Harriet and Jane, then,

"Thisbe's oldest son is Walter, and he and I have made a pretty fine ranch out of a patch of sage brush. Though Walter is married, I have yet plenty of help with Sidney, twelve, and Ray, nine, and Art still coming on for my old age."

"Well, I'll be damned," snorted Pete, coming down on the front legs of the Congress chair with a bang. "You've got it all planned out."

"Besides," Eph went on, "each mother gets help inside the house from her girls. You see we Mormons have a great advantage with our big, well-trained families. The older ones unselfishly help the little ones, and we don't have anything to do but work and be happy."

"Yeah, but," interrupted Pete, "you've only got one wife now."

Mack moved in easily beside Eph, "Why don't you teach your children your prophets can be wrong?"

"Mack Armstrong, I would rather have my right arm cut off right there," stated Eph, putting his other hand on his arm just below the shoulder, "than to teach my children false doctrine."

"But hold on, Hanks!" Mack sprang to his feet. "Your Articles of Faith by Joseph Smith, your prophet, say that you believe in 'obeying, honoring, and sustaining the law.' "

"I do. And that is why when the Edmund-Tucker Law became effective and was declared by the Supreme Court to be constitutional, I called my Thisbe and Jane together and laid the situation before them. I have fought for my country and the Constitution," Eph continued quietly, "and I do not want my children to lose faith in that great document."

"What did your wives do?" asked Mack.

"Jane Capener chose to get a divorce, which the court granted her free." Eph reminded the marshals that Harriet had already divorced him, leaving only Thisbe as his wife.

"So, you're in the clear! We can't touch you," grumbled Pete, "Too bad."

"And I'll bet you support and render comfort to all of them and their children," said Mack.

"Well, a man naturally does what he can." He looked up the canyon, shadowed eerily in the moonlight.

The deputy marshals glanced at the pleasant five-room house, which was the largest and finest in Wayne County. It was a frame house, lined with adobe and plaster, warm in the winter and cool in the summer. All the rustic work was made with a hand plane.

Pete grinned and nudged Mack, "And we have a hard time keeping one wife and two kids apiece."

Sidney, on the front room floor, grew suddenly sleepy. He cuddled down beside his slumbering brother and drew a long breath. In his heart surged a love for his father and a deep sense of gratitude for his father's honor, for he chose to sustain his government as well as the Articles of Faith. Sidney felt very secure. He was no longer afraid of the two marshals—or anybody!

# 15

# EPH HANKS, PATRIARCH

The isolated Hanks home was miles from the scattered ranches and small settlements in Wayne County. Seven miles separated it from the main highway. Hanks Hospitality Ranch was an ideal stopover for travelers and pleasure-seekers. They enjoyed Thisbe's delicious meals and the genuine hospitality of the Hanks home. The roads were rough and rutted, and the distance was approximately the same between the larger settlements from whence the visitors came. People traveled mostly in lumber wagons or horseback. There were very few buggies in the county. When a white-topped buggy drove in, the children knew their visitors were special and scampered into the house to tell the news to their mother or to the barn where they informed their father. The Wayne Stake presidency rode in one of these exciting buggies. They always spent a delightful evening with Eph Hanks and family when they were out visiting the wards and branches in the eastern end of the stake. The president of the stake invariably would say their trip was not complete without the hearty hand-clasp, the interesting experiences, and delightful entertainment of Eph Hanks and his family. They enthusiastically declared they would gladly go miles farther and pay admission to be entertained by the talented Hanks family. Thisbe and all the children cultivated a taste for entertaining, as they were deprived of the social side of community life.

The organ was played by each one. Although no music teacher was available, cards with chords on were placed above the keys to accompany singing or musical instruments. Often nearby ranchers rode miles for an evening's entertainment. Trappers and prospectors often enjoyed the fun, which to them was welcome diversion from the lonely hours spent in the hills or on the river. The happy atmosphere and spirit of the Hanks home made everyone feel at ease.

Old Colorado Ed, a river rat from the deep gorges of the Colorado River, would call at the Floral Ranch four times a year when he went for supplies and returned. With him was a large reddish-brown Newfoundland dog named Sport. Sport was a trick dog and gave the Hanks family much amusement. At Ed's order, Sport would hold a piece of meat on his nose until the count of three. Then he would toss it in the air and catch it in his mouth. Sport jumped as high as Ed's head and spun through a hoop without touching it.

Were Ed to hold the hoop side-wise, Sport would leap over it and under it.

The Hanks children enjoyed hearing Ed tell of how Sport saved his bedding, grubstake, and guns when the rope he had tied to his river boat broke, letting the boat loose. It was carried down the river in the boiling current. Old Ed hollered, "Catch it, Sport, catch it!" Sport plunged into the roaring, rapidly flowing stream. Ed stripped off his shoes and pants and ran desperately down the sandy bank to swim out and grab the boat. Sport swam and grabbed the dangling rope in his teeth as Ed lunged into the water and saved the boat and his supplies. Sport was a favorite at the Hanks ranch. They loved him almost as much as they loved his master, Ed.

After supper and the evening work was done, the family would invite Ed, who had a good singing voice, to join them in a "sing-song." Quite often old Ed would sing a few ballads by himself.

One day Colorado Ed came to Floral Ranch without Sport. Old Sport had picked up strychnine bait that had been set out for the coyotes. Ed worked over his pet and did everything possible to save his life, but the dog died in his arms out on a lonely spot in the desert. He held a sad ceremony over Sport's remains, putting his best coat over the body, and he buried Sport in a well-marked grave. Ed made a number of trips to Floral Ranch, but it was more than a year before he could sing any of the old songs without shedding tears for his pal, Sport.

Eph Hanks was a sound disciplinarian. His children perceived that he was fair and just, yet at times they got the better of him. One afternoon when Arthur wanted Nettie to go to the house and bring him a slice of bread spread with jam, she refused to go. He picked up a rock and hit her between the shoulders. Father Hanks brought Art to him and demanded an explanation. His son insisted he had not thrown the rock at her. "She just humped up her back and let it hit her!" This surprising interpretation brought a smile to his father's face and lessened the boy's punishment.

One day Sidney and Ray let their tempers flare and engaged in a clod fight. Sidney lobbed a hard clod at Ray and struck him in the forehead as Father Hanks walked around the corner of the house and yelled at them. The clod throwing stopped abruptly when their father spoke of how wicked it was for brothers to fight. "You have read about Cain and Abel and that Jesus said to love one another," he reminded them. The boys, with sheepish looks on their faces, dropped the clods they held in their hands. Each stammered out an explanation of how the trouble started—each boy placing the blame on his brother.

"Well," wisely said Father Eph, rubbing his chin, "I think I can settle the argument. Go and cut me two long willow switches. Ray, you cut one you'd like to see me use on Sid, and, Sid, cut one that would be good medicine for Ray. Don't be gone long."

Along the irrigation ditch grew willows in abundance. The boys felt very silly when they returned to their father with switches and heard him say, "Now, square off and change willows. You may stop whenever you wear out the willow switch. Don't strike above the belt. Five free licks against the first one who fouls."

The legs of both boys were bare to the knees. Swish, swish sounded the willow switches as each boy whipped a stinging blow around bony legs, and the trousers proved very thin below the belt. The brothers put up an enthusiastic fight for a few minutes until each one commenced to grab the other's willow to break off the slender portion of the stinging switch. Soon each willow was of no use to continue the fight. Each boy whined a sullen "No!" when Father Hanks asked if they wanted freshly cut switches. "Well, you'd better shake hands, then, and call it square."

Sidney later recalled the incident and said. "Ray and I were near of a size and got along okay until one or the other of us got bossy. Then sometimes we'd have a friendly fight. But you can tell the world we never called on Father to settle any of our fights after that."

One day as Ray was in the field irrigating the crops, he noticed Old Dopey, a gentle loco horse, standing asleep in a patch of alfalfa. Being as athletically talented as his father, he ran up behind Old Dopey, dug his shovel in the soft earth, and vaulted onto the horse's back. Taken by surprise, possibly surmising that a mountain lion had pounced on his back, Old Dopey reared five feet. The burst of sudden energy was just too much for Ray who spun off the animal's back and struck the alfalfa some ten feet from where he had been hurled into the air. Dopey ran with lightning speed through the corral onto the high ground across the creek. There he snorted and pawed the ground the whole day long.

Eph laughingly remarked to Ray that he did not know Old Dopey had so much vinegar left in his tough old hide. The family had considerable difficulty deciding which was the more surprised—Old Dopey or Ray.

While living at Floral Ranch, Eph's reputation for healing spread throughout the southern Utah settlements. Walter's wife, Mary Ellen, accompanied Eph on many of his errands to the sick. Eph performed many instant healings. In June, 1894, the wife of George W. Carrell was very sick. Her husband felt her days upon the earth were numbered. She requested to have Brother Hanks come and administer to her, but Eph was in a settlement fifteen miles away. About eleven o'clock that night the door opened and in walked Eph Hanks. He immediately walked over to the bed whereon lay Carrell's sick wife. Looking down upon her languid countenance, he said softly, "You are sick, aren't you? Just as I thought. Where is your oil?"

She told him where the oil was in the cupboard, and he walked over and picked up the vessel of consecrated oil. Back at the bedside, he anointed her head with oil and administered to her. After performing this sacred ordinance, he said, "Sister Carrell, now you are made well by the power of God. I am very weak and hungry. Please get up and get me something to eat." Mrs. Carrell requested her robe and slippers be brought her. Soon she had prepared a tasty supper for her benefactor.

Prayer was a practical reality in Eph Hanks's life. To Eph, morning prayer with his family kneeling around was the key that opened the treasurehouse of God's mercies and blessings; and their evening prayer was the key that kept them up under his protection. He taught his children "Leave not off praying to God, for either praying will make you leave off sinning; or continuing to sin will make you desist from praying." He often alluded to the words of Tennyson, "More things are wrought by prayer than this world dreams of." To Eph, prayer meant just as Jesus enjoined, "Ask and it shall be given you." He verified this by his life experiences. Prayer to Eph was a source of self-generating energy.

On one occasion, Eph was miles away from his home when word came to him that his daughter, Georgenia, was extremely ill. He mounted his horse and galloped toward Floral Ranch through sleet and snow. Scarcely had he started on his way when the horse he was riding became sick and could go no farther. Eph bowed his head and invoked the blessings of God on the horse. The pony revived and carried his master safely home. He administered to Georgenia, who continued to worsen instead of recovering. Eph visited each of his neighbors and asked them to fast with him and Thisbe for the recovery of Georgenia. Each one of his neighbors repented of his or her sins and promised God to do better. Georgenia was healed. She lived to be a mother of three children.

One spring on the new ranch, Eph and his sons, Walter and Sidney, were planting corn along Pleasant

Creek. The Hanks family had been without meat for a month. That evening Walter took the only rifle owned by his father and walked into the nearby foothills in the hope of getting some venison. Eph instructed Sidney to build a fire, "Walter will soon bring home meat, and we'll have a good supper." Three shots rang out from the foothills. Eph came to the cabin and filled the kettle full of water, hanging it on the crane above the fire. Eph and Sidney patiently waited for Walter to bring the venison to drop into the kettle.

When Walter walked into the cabin with no kill, he told how he had crippled a deer first shot, but, being unable to get his nerves settled, fired the other shots as wild as the deer he was firing at.

Eph's blue eyes blazed as he turned to Walter and said, "I'm surprised at your throwing away all that ammunition. You must have had a strong attack of buck fever." Then calmly he asked, "Did you think to pray before you went after that deer?" Walter shook his head. Eph had driven home a valuable lesson Walter never forgot.

A few years after this incident, Eph took Sidney into the mountains hunting deer. They sighted a small herd of mule deer some distance away. Sidney held the horses while his father slipped from the saddle and noiselessly walked through the quaking aspen toward the game. Quite a distance from Sid, he dropped to his knees for a moment. Sidney, observing his father's prayer, bowed his head. Eph quietly arose, took careful aim, and brought down a large buck which, with Sidney's help, he threw on the burro and tied securely.

The two men helped the burro with the heavy load.

Eph's willingness to accept counsel from the leaders of the Church was an admirable characteristic of this king of the western scouts. While living at Floral Ranch on Pleasant Creek, Walter, a bishop at the time, suggested Eph and Thisbe move to Cainesville for the winter. Looking his son squarely in the eye, Eph asked, "Is this my son, Walter, who is asking his father to move from Floral Ranch to Cainesville, or is it the bishop of the Cainesville Ward?" When Walter assured his father he was speaking as the bishop, Eph moved from his comfortable ranch home to Cainesville for the winter as advised.

In his earlier years, Eph learned he was being seriously considered for the office of bishop in a small town south of Salt Lake City. Whatever his reasons for not wanting to accept the calling, Eph resorted to a bit of chicanery. Learning that the stake presidency was meeting on a Saturday night to decide on the bishop of the ward, Eph tied tin cans to his horse's tail and rode up and down the street in front of the meeting house, hollering unintelligibly. The following day he smiled happily when the stake president selected another man for the position.

Eph could go from the sublime to the ridiculous probably as quickly and with as little effort as any man who ever lived, no matter what the conditions were. Eph had an old man by the name of Bill Braffett working for him. Braffett was a conceited, bald chap. He boasted one day that he could do anything Eph could do. Eph was skinning an ox at the time. When he came to the skin on the back of the animal's neck, he cut out a piece about two inches wide and twelve inches long. He scraped the hair off and split it in two and then asked Bill to take his choice. Braffett, sensing what Eph had in mind, chose the smaller piece. Eph, turning to his hired man, said, "Now, Bill, go to it, and we will see which of us can eat this hide in the shortest time." In less than ten minutes, Eph had eaten the last morsel of rawhide. Walking over to where Bill was standing, he inquired, "What's become of your portion of old Blue's neck?"

"Why, Eph, I've eaten it long ago." The words had hardly escaped his lips when Eph pulled the one-by-twelve inch strip of rawhide out from under Braffett's shirt.

If there were a turning point in Eph's life when he reflected seriously about his past, it could have been in the spring of 1893 when he loaded some sacks of grain into his light spring wagon and started for the grist mill located on the Fremont River near Bicknell. It had been a meatless winter for the hardy pioneer. The day before Eph arrived, the miller had butchered a few hogs. As Eph unloaded his grain, the miller informed him that he had dressed a number of hogs and he could help himself to the fresh pork. Most of the night Eph sat up, cooking and eating pork. To him it was like the good old days on the plains when the friendly Indians led him from one wigwam to another, wherein he feasted with each of the chiefs.

Next morning he loaded the flour into his wagon and started back to the ranch. Before he reached his ranch, Eph was a very sick man. He was helped into bed where he remained feverish and in pain for months, and it seemed his recovery was impossible. As the fever burned itself out, he talked of the man in the gray tweeds who had just left his bedside and eased himself through the wall as a fog lifts from the valley to float into space. A little later he asked Thisbe to read the story of Abraham to him. He saw his own life paralleling that of the ancient patriarch. During those weeks when Eph lay on his bed in a painfully helpless condition, his mind slowly walked him back through the years and he relived those hazardous days of privation and hardships. Often he awakened in the midst of a dream of a harrowing experience, and his body was weak and perspiring.

When he was well enough to read for himself, he perused the accounts of Abraham, Moses, and Job, ending with the story of Lehi and Nephi and their trials and tribulations leaving Jerusalem and journeying to the Promised Land. To Eph the heavens were opened, and it was revealed to him the great plan of happiness to man. Unfolded before him were the powers of heaven and the connecting link with the rights of the priesthood given to man. The vision was complete and beautiful, giving the king of the western scouts strength and courage to live and do his part.

Finally, he was hobbling about. How wonderful the Pleasant River Valley looked to him. His heart sang out in praises to the God of his salvation. Outdoors, he called Sidney to him and requested him to saddle his pony and lead it to the front door. Eph, bundled in his heavy overcoat, mounted and rode off for the south draw, the winter cattle range. About an hour later he returned and called to Sidney to help him off his mount. He wearily sank into a custom chair, closed his eyes, and whispered, "Thy will be done!" Quietly he dropped off to sleep, at peace with the world and satisfied that he had given his Lord full allegiance.

While recovering from this near fatal illness, Eph was in a most somber and contemplative mood. He resolved to make a tribute to the Lord, some token of gratitude that his life had been spared. Cattle were precious possessions. To lose a cow or a steer brought sorrow to the family. Old Darb, his prize bull, he had raised from a wobbly calf and tamed so the children could fondly touch the huge bovine. They took turns playing on his back when he laid down or riding him while driving the cattle to the corrals.

Spring burst with robins strutting on the lawn, pulling up worms from the greening grass. A light shower had changed the tones from drab yellow to emerald. Eph's cattle had been taken to browse in the hollow valleys beyond the ranch house. Eph was much improved, the children were through school, and Thisbe was happy and relieved that her husband was well and about. The boys rode up the south draw to gather the dry cattle. Old Darb and a favorite cow were missing. The boys searched for the missing stock. They were shocked, saddened, and angered to find Old Darb and the cow with bullet holes in their skulls. Some careless hunter had deliberately killed their favorite cattle. The boys hurriedly rode to the ranchhouse and excitedly told their father. There was grief in the Hanks family, and the neighbors also emotionally suffered for the loss. Eph simply said, "Too bad! They got in the way of a bullet." It was not until after his death that Thisbe, to whom he had confided, revealed that he had offered as a sacrifice to the Lord the finest cattle that he had. This was his way of showing the Lord that his repentance was complete. His heart was at peace.

Eph had served his church and the people with little regard for his personal welfare. His best days were spent in service. He had no regrets. To him it was a joy to serve the Lord's people and help them get settled along the Wasatch range, to make peace with the Indians, and to be obedient to the prophets.

In August, 1893, President Wilford Woodruff sent the apostle, Brigham Young, Jr., to Wayne Stake, and he ordained Eph Hanks a patriarch. Eph was sixty-seven. During his first two years as patriarch to the Wayne Stake he gave 120 blessings and "...taught the gospel to his fellow men continually." Eph magnified his calling with little difficulty. He spent the remainder of his life blessing the people, serving them as the Lord's anointed, by setting an example in righteous living. He spoke in ward sacrament meetings and in stake conferences. Summaries of his talks recorded by ward and stake clerks over a three-year period, show that his calling as patriarch suited him very well.

As a speaker, Eph was unique. His speaking style, according to a contemporary, Dave Rust, was very much like J. Golden Kimball's. His favorite themes were fasting and prayer, following the counsel of Church

authorities, and missionary work. Once in a stake conference, "Patriarch E. K. Hanks thought it wise to watch
as well as pray...related one experience encountered
during the Johnston Army War, illustrating the necessity of being watchful...said every elder should be a prophet and patriarch to his family...asked for the prayers
of the Saints and encouraged them to keep command-
ments of God...related a dream the Lord gave him
years ago demonstrating the way the Lord makes provisions for His Saints in time of need." Eph believed
"If you keep the counsel of the apostles you will never
lack for bread." To Eph, as expressed in his sermons,
"There is no greater honor than to preach the gospel
of Jesus Christ and to encourage the youth to prepare
themselves for foreign missions."

Following Eph's brush with death, his first concern
was to his family and to honor his calling as patriarch.
He was well enough to work on the farm and to attend church activities, but he continued slowly losing
his strength. The body that he had repeatedly pushed
to the breaking point during more than 50,000 miles
of travel, hundreds of peace missions to the Indians,
and the rescue of the handcart pioneers seemed at last
to respond to years of abuse. Realizing that her husband was failing rapidly, Thisbe arranged a surprise
birthday party and family reunion in his honor on
March 20, 1896.

Twenty-eight family members gathered at Floral
Ranch. One reported, "Refreshments were served after
which Brother Hanks exhorted all to be honest, virtuous, and live upright lives, always praying so that

they might always walk in the light of the gospel. He selected some of his experiences and bore a powerful testimony to the truth of the gospel."

A week following his birthday, Eph was thrown from a horse he was breaking, and Thisbe put him to bed with a severe pain in his head. After a brief period of intense suffering, he rallied for a few days until the pain spread to his legs and they became numb. Just before his noble spirit took flight to the paradise of God, he sat up and spoke excitedly. His loving family at the bedside knew from his words that the dying man had a vision of the man in gray tweeds entering the room on his white charger and leading an exquisitely white mount neatly equipped. The mystery man smiled and gave the signal. Eph settled back and relaxed in the arms of his son, Walter, smiled his approval, and went peacefully to his last sleep.

Friends and admirers gathered throughout the area to pay Eph homage. What probably pleased Eph most was the guard of one thousand Indians who stood, rimming the ledge above the ranch in silent tribute to their friend and brother, Eph, the peacemaker. A fit tribute to a man who loved them.

One reporter in attendance at Eph's funeral penned: "Such a sweet, heavenly influence was there that one did not feel to mourn. Those present testified that it was beyond anything they had ever witnessed. It made one think as the Apostle Paul, 'O death, where is thy sting? O grave, where is thy victory?' "

Solomon F. Kimball, a close associate of Eph, paid him tribute:

"He was naturally intelligent, God-fearing, and liberal to a fault. Of course, he was somewhat rough, as he had but little opportunity to attend school or to enjoy the comforts of home life. He was good at relating stories and never permitted a point to be lost in the story's telling. Under the most trying circumstances he was always cheerful, and scarce a word of complaining was ever heard to come from his lips. His life was marvelously and often miraculously spared while he passed through terrible danger. This generation of Latter-day Saints will never fully appreciate what this king of scouts did toward the establishment of this Church in these valleys until the books spoken of in the revelation of John shall have been opened. When the dead, small and great, stand before God to be judged according to their works, Father Hanks will be found in the front ranks among the noble and great, which came out of great tribulation."